BETTER DEAD THAN DIVORCED

THE TRIALS OF PANAYOTA: A TRUE STORY

October 22, 2020

Dear chinnell,

Best wishes

Lukas

LUKAS KONANDREAS M.D.

TABLE OF CONTENTS

Acknowledgments 1

Foreword 3

Prologue 10

Part I 13

Chapter 1: The Test 15

Chapter 2: Tired of Secrets 21

Chapter 3: Married or Tarnished 24

Chapter 4: Omen 28

Chapter 5: Dark Days 32

Chapter 6: Kolito 35

Chapter 7: Flirting 42

Chapter 8: Shining Star of the Sky 46

Chapter 9: Dead Serious 50

Chapter 10: No Deal 55

Part II 57

Chapter 11: Guardian Angel 59

Chapter 12: Business Partners And Opposites 64

Chapter 13: Best Friends 70

Chapter 14: Heart In the Right Place 75

Chapter 15: Then You Would Know.............................79
Chapter 16: Nobody to Talk to..............................83

Part III...**87**
Chapter 17: Cracks In the Façade...........................89
Chapter 18: In the Shadow of Pyrgos........................92
Chapter 19: Fumbling In the Dark...........................96
Chapter 20: "You Have Devoured Me."........................100
Chapter 21: A Job for the Police...........................106
Chapter 22: The Police Want You............................111
Chapter 23: A Village Divided..............................116
Chapter 24: A Check from Australia.........................122
Chapter 25: A Pistol In the Pocket.........................127
Chapter 26: The Signature..................................133

Part IV..**139**
Chapter 27: To The Court In Athens.........................141
Chapter 28: With Honor And Conscience?.....................149
Chapter 29: Periplanumeni..................................154
Chapter 30: Corrupt court..................................160
Chapter 31: Honest and Straightforward.....................164
Chapter 32: George's Mistress Takes the Stand..............168
Chapter 33: First-Hand News................................174
Chapter 34: The List.......................................177
Chapter 35: Influence......................................183
Chapter 36: Experts..187
Chapter 37: Vendetta.......................................191
Chapter 38: An Act...195
Chapter 39: the 9:1 Verdict................................202
Chapter 40: Family Pressures...............................206
Chapter 41: The Attorney General...........................209

Part V...**213**
Chapter 42: To Halkida For Justice?........................215
Chapter 43: "Straight in the village, crooked in court."...221
Chapter 44: Is This the Famous Katina?.....................228
Chapter 45: "Just one day".................................231
Chapter 46: Surprise.......................................236
Chapter 47: Think of Your Child............................241
Chapter 48: "Are You Not George Nitsos?"...................246

Chapter 49: No Punishment Too Harsh..............253
Chapter 50: A Marriage Made in Heaven..............257
Chapter 51: The Best Defense..............260
Chapter 52: Theatrics..............265
Chapter 53: Message From Darkness_darkness Overcome?..............268
Chapter 54: The Telegram..............272

Part VI: Life After The Courts..............**275**
Chapter 55: The Bones of the Dead..............277
Chapter 56: The Night Visit..............281
Chapter 57: At Last a Dowry!..............284
Epilogue..............287
Afterword..............290
Dramatis Personae..............296

PROLOGUE

I awoke with a start. Fearfully clinging to me—almost choking me—was my younger brother Panos.

"What's happening?" he cried.

"I don't know."

Our tiny village of Kupaki had been reverberating all night with the merry din emanating from two parties—one at the Zakkas's home, several houses down from us, and one at the Kumes's home, which sat equidistant from our house in the opposite direction. Summer was drawing to a close, and on this mild September night in 1953, my siblings and I had drifted off to the sounds of music, laughter, and dancing, only to be woken minutes later by the menacing peal of gunshots.

Now voices could be heard shouting in the darkness. "George!" several partygoers hollered. "Is that you? Are you okay?"

"Help!" a man called back, his voice a distant echo in the tangle of narrow streets. "They are trying to kill us! They are trying to kill us!"

"*Mama! Baba!*" I asked, unable to calm my quavering voice. "What's going on?"

Panos and I, too afraid to leave the safety of our old, dilapidated bed, were soon joined by our older brother Kostas, who had also been calling to our parents. Now we gathered in the darkness, waiting for a response.

My parents didn't answer, although I could hear them hurriedly dressing in their room.

"The bastard has killed her," Thanasis muttered angrily before rushing outside with Polyxeni.

Who? I wondered fearfully. *Who is the bastard? And who has he killed?* My mind raced as I tried to piece together what little I knew. Father had come home late, after we had fallen asleep at around 10:30 p.m. He was always the last one home, since he had to lock up the

CHAPTER 1:
THE TEST

FROM THE MOMENT SHE BLOSSOMED into a beautiful young woman, trouble seemed to follow Panayota wherever she went. And that trouble, I'm sure Thanasis would have insisted, had a name: George Nitsos. Charming, gregarious, slippery—George Nitsos had no regard for the conservative mores of rural Greece. He was the kind of young man who inspired fathers to keep their daughters under lock and key, the kind of young man whose smile said one thing while his eyes said another. After he took an interest in my aunt, it wasn't long before she found herself the subject of village gossip.

Thanasis was serving as Panayota's chaperone the night she was forced to reveal a terrible secret to her family.

"Are you ready?" he asked after helping her dismount from his horse.

It was still the 1930s. I wasn't yet a gleam in Thanasis's eye. At the moment, his gaze rested on his frightened cousin, who he knew was about to receive a severe tongue-lashing from the rest of the family. Though he didn't approve of Panayota's errant ways, Thanasis nevertheless felt sympathy for her plight. The two had just returned from the nearby village of Krokylion, where she had met with a doctor at his office for her second virginity test. The first test, conducted weeks earlier under nebulous conditions, had yielded unclear results and had earned the headstrong young girl a stern reprimand from her family. This time, however, the findings were incontrovertible: she was no virgin.

"Yes," Panayota said nervously.

Thanasis nodded stoically and turned to secure his horse outside the Soulias family's two-story stone residence. The house was much like the other houses in Kupaki which had gray stone walls, a Spartan balcony overlooking the terraced village, roof tiles the color of burnt sienna, two bedrooms, one or two fireplaces, a living room, and a kitchen. A cellar or a separate smaller structure was used to store the locally produced food supplies, the horse or the mule, a goat or two, a few chickens, and a pig. There was no running water and no electricity in any of the homes.

Panayota disappeared inside to face her family.

Thanasis, hoping to spare Panayota the prying eyes and wagging tongues of her fellow villagers, had waited for darkness to fall before escorting her home on his horse. During the ride, Panayota had admitted she'd indeed had sex with George. She liked him. He had pledged to marry her. There was only one solution, thought Thanasis, still trying to shake off the embarrassment he'd felt at the doctor's office: George would have to make good on his promise.

Unfortunately, nothing could be done to protect Panayota from her family's scorn. By the time Thanasis had followed his cousin inside, every adult member of the Soulias and Konandreas families—her mother, siblings, grandparents, aunts, uncles, cousins—was looking at her expectantly. Had she failed the test?

Panayota circa 1935

Panayota circa 1940.

Panayota, staring at her feet, spoke in a hushed tone. "The doctor said I'm not a virgin."

Thanasis found the tension nearly unbearable. Would they chop her into pieces and throw her into the brook, as one of her elders had warned her only a few short weeks ago? He suspected such talk was exaggerated, but he also knew the emotions that fueled it were combustible.

Who would speak first? Paraskevi, Panayota's widowed mother? One of her uncles or aunts? A grandparent? A cousin? What kind of invective would they spit at the fearless young girl?

Metsios, Panayota's younger brother, was the first to react, but not with words. He leapt at his sister, shoving her violently toward the fireplace.

Panayota lost her balance and fell backward into the burning embers.

While Thanasis and the other men rushed forward to restrain Metsios, a screaming Panayota pulled herself from the fireplace with the help of the women, who were now furiously beating the flames from the girl's clothing. Singed but not seriously injured, she turned and fled outside as soon as the flames had been tamped out, leaving behind the stench of burnt fabric.

Paraskevi, still screaming in horror, could barely be heard above the men-folk, most of whom continued to unleash a blue streak of vitriol even after Panayota's tearful exit.

"I'm going to kill Linatsas!" thundered Metsios, whose curses were now aimed equally at his sister and his best friend.

Known by many in the village as "Linatsas," George Nitsos had earned the nickname after purportedly being caught red-handed stealing a lamb, which, according to legend, he had tried to smuggle away in a burlap bag, or *linatsa*. Although he would deny the story to his dying day, it would nevertheless haunt him throughout his life.

"Why did I let the bastard into my house?" Metsios growled.

One of eight children, George hailed from Kupaki, although his father was often absent, having traveled to America to find work. For a short stretch in the 1920s, the Nitsos family had returned to Greece but on their next trip back to America, George was left behind and returned with a few of his siblings to Kupaki.

"Why did his father leave him behind?" Metsios lamented. "Couldn't he have taken him to America?"

George's homecoming had reunited him with Metsios, his old classmate and good friend. Not long afterward, George had met Metsios's fetching older sister, and Panayota had been courting trouble ever since.

"I'm going to kill him," Metsios repeated, only with less conviction now and in a much softer voice. As he spoke, he stared out the window to the west in the direction of George's house, which was only 150 yards away. He was beginning to calm down.

It helped that the women were urging him to keep quiet, lest he be heard by neighbors and add insult to humiliation.

Thanasis and the other men in the room released Metsios from their collective grip, and soon the room fell silent.

Aggelo, Thanasis's sister, was the first to speak up. She leveled an accusatory stare at Metsios. "Do you know what you have done?"

"I don't care," he muttered angrily. "Let her go to hell forever."

"Metsios, can you hear what you're saying? What will you do if your sister throws herself down the ravine?"

Metsios flinched visibly. Was he finally coming to his senses?

As Thanasis studied the young man's round, innocent face for clues, he tried to put himself in Metsios's shoes. How would he feel if his best friend had shamed his sister? Would he feel duped? Betrayed? He would certainly be brimming with anger. It was obvious that George had viewed his friendship with Metsios as a way to his sister's heart. Though they were the same age, Metsios clearly looked up to George. His wide-eyed admiration served as silent applause to George, for whom life was a performance. George had always struck Thanasis as the kind of performer whose self-esteem sky-rocketed or nosedived according to his audience's response. In Metsios, he could count on rapt admiration.

George was the friendly extrovert who knew all about life in the big city, the sophisticate who could tell a seemingly serious story with a straight face until delivering the punch line, which never failed to double over his listeners with laughter. He didn't boast of his family in America. Instead, he poked fun at their respectability in a good-natured way. He was generous with his friends, often sharing the American dollars that his father mailed to him. For many shy young men, to pal around with George Nitsos was to bask in reflected glory; it was an easy way to earn the attention of the opposite sex without committing to the hard work of courtship or risking the rejection that came with it. The village girls, meanwhile, couldn't resist his boyish charm. He was effusive with his praise, often lavishing it on the fairer sex with such hyperbole that it bordered on the ludicrous. The conservative community of Kupaki, on the other hand, frowned when young girls accepted the overtures of this rogue with nothing more than a smile and a blush.

"Oh, my girl, my girl," Paraskevi lamented.

"I'll go and look for her myself," Aggelo said. "All of you just try to keep quiet. And don't start another round of weeping and swearing. You'll have the whole village talking about this for months."

"Do you need a flashlight, Aggelo?" Metsios asked.

Thanasis's sister, still clearly peeved, rolled her eyes. "You think of everything, don't you, Metsios?" she said in a sweet voice laced with acerbic undertones. "Now that you've taken care of all the other things, maybe I should just run this little errand of finding your sister before she kills herself."

With that, Aggelo stepped out into the darkness.

Before beginning her search for Panayota, Aggelo made a mental checklist of all the locations where the desperate girl might go to hide. Every village had places where people could go when they wanted to be alone, and Kupaki was no different. She would start with the village spring of Motsu, which vibrated with gossip and energy during the waking hours but was a solemn, peaceful haven at night. It was near Panayota's home, near where she worked, and offered several hiding places beneath the canopy of trees.

First, she needed to catch her breath. She leaned back against the trunk of an ancient maple tree and waited for her breathing to slow down and her eyes to adjust to the darkness, the spring gurgling just a few feet away.

Paraskevi's lament—"Oh, my girl, my girl"—echoed in Aggelo's mind. Not so long ago, Panayota had been an innocent young girl, someone who worked hard at school and at home. Always well groomed and neatly dressed, she was known for her sense of humor. People talked of the second Soulias girl's *tsahpina*, a nearly untranslatable Greek word that encompassed graciousness, efficiency, and elegance. Now she was hiding in the dark, a blot on her family's honor.

Aggelo listened quietly for an exhale or a sob that would lead her to her cousin. Soon she heard footsteps coming toward her. They were too heavy to belong to Panayota, who was small, slim, and light-footed. This was the heavy tread of a man. Her heart skipped a beat at the thought of being caught outside without a male chaperone. What madness had inspired this adventure? Why hadn't she asked her brother Thanasis or one of the other men to set off in search of Panayota?

The answer, she knew, was a simple one: her cousin would be more likely to trust her.

When the man closed to within a few feet, Aggelo breathed a sigh of relief. It was Metsios.

"Hey!" she whispered.

Her cousin let out a terrified cry, clutching his chest. Then, after taking a few seconds to calm himself, he joined Aggelo against the same stout maple trunk. As he did, he launched into a five-minute tirade that made use of every curse in the Greek language.

Aggelo waited for him to finish. "Don't you think you've done enough?" she scolded him. "You're the last person Panayota will want to talk to if she's somewhere out here. Do us all a favor and go home."

To Aggelo's relief, Metsios did just that. As soon as he was safely on his way, she took a few tentative steps, just enough to escape the noise from the gurgling spring. Then she whistled softly, imitating the call of a nightingale, and waited.

CHAPTER 2:
TIRED OF SECRETS

PANAYOTA HAD FOUND A HIDING place in her uncle's terraced garden, just below the springs, where she sat on a rock and leaned against one of the stone walls, waiting silently. Stars lit up the night sky. Fireflies hovered and danced in the cool night air. On distant hilltops, shepherds stoked fires to stay warm and keep the jackals at bay. Nearly every home in the village had a vegetable patch, not to mention stairs and balconies decorated with potted flowers, vegetables, and basil—all of which filled the air with a heady fragrance. The ripening fruit from trees, too, could be detected in the cool breeze. But nothing compared to the pungent aroma of honeysuckle, which was particularly powerful at night and filled Panayota's nostrils with its sweet scent.

She was still shocked by the savagery of her brother's response, still numb from the indignity of being forced to endure not one but two virginity tests. Was it a crime to love George Nitsos? Part of her wanted to answer Aggelo's soft whistle, but part of her wanted only to run away with her lover, to disappear forever. Then again, sometimes she wished she'd never met George Nitsos. Before he had come along, life had been so much simpler.

She had met George not long after going to work for the neighbors, the Koinis family, who had offered to take care of her in return for her help with household chores and work in the fields. Her mother, after mulling over the idea, had consented. Life had been hard since her father's passing, and Paraskevi had no doubt thought she was giving Panayota, just thirteen at the time, an opportunity at a better life. And she had been right. Panayota had fit in right away with Koinogiorgos and his family, who never mistreated her.

Then one day Panayota met her brother's friend, George. Handsome, lean, charismatic, George was a consummate flirt and often said things that made the young girl's face blush and her heart race. The two began seeing each other secretly, meeting in the vineyards near the spring of Motsu, which was perfectly situated between the Koinis house and her home. As the tone and content of their conversations grew more intimate, Panayota suddenly realized one day that she was being courted—and that she was enjoying these clandestine rendezvouses.

When word of their affair reached her mother, brother, and her cousins, the Konandreases, Panayota earned an earful. She was called a slut and told she had dishonored her family. When she revealed the truth, which was that she had done nothing to compromise her innocence, she was met with distrust and contempt. Metsios had recommended she be seen by a doctor, who would be able to prove or disprove her claims of innocence. The virginity test, however, had yielded murky results, which the doctor had blamed on poor lighting and a lack of necessary equipment.

Panayota, still leaning against the stone wall in the darkness, flinched involuntarily. The memory of her first virginity test still sent her flesh crawling. She had been so terrified during the test that the doctor had admonished her for her lack of proper cooperation, which he had said had marred the results. Not that anything had changed after the test. George, after staying away for a while to avoid further inflaming Panayota's family as well as the Koinises, returned at the time of the wheat harvest. During the noonday siesta, he could be heard crooning a love song to Panayota:

"Vipers hissing venomous wrath
Keep my love and me apart.
But I'll cross their spiteful path
To be with you, my sweetheart."

Panayota didn't think her family or the Koinises were snakes, of course. They were merely trying to protect her honor, along with their own reputations as upstanding members of the community. The Koinises, intent on avoiding further scandal, had put in place several restrictions to curb Panayota's behavior and had begun watching her closely. Just like her family, they felt impugned by George's indecent behavior.

But Panayota nevertheless admired her suitor's temerity. She began meeting him again, only now under the cover of darkness, furtively seeking his embraces in the vineyards and vegetable gardens in the neighborhood. After the Koinises caught Panayota sneaking out one night for another rendezvous, the same drama played out once more: admonishment, followed by denial, followed by a virginity test.

This time, though, the doctor's findings had left no room for doubt. She had dishonored her family.

Panayota, shivering in the cool night air, wrapped herself in her arms. She knew that she had no power to change things. She was a woman. George was a man. They lived by two different codes. While he could prowl the neighborhood with impunity, she could only be seen in public with a male chaperone. Even in the house of God, men and women were segregated. Matches were made by parents and elders, not by young lovers. Compatibility was determined by financial and social status, work ethic, and overall character, not by a meeting of the eyes or the spark ignited by a first kiss. A prospective bride's value was gauged by how much her family could offer in the way of a dowry, and a groom's value hinged on his ability to provide for a family. Both were expected to be God-fearing, respectful of traditions, and obedient toward their elders.

George had sullied her reputation, but there was still a chance he might choose to marry her—as he had promised. The men in her family, Panayota knew, would be duty-bound to make sure he did exactly that. Her only other choice was to recede into the shadows and hope that people might one day forget, or at least forgive, her indiscretions. Otherwise, she would carry the shame of her illicit romance for the rest of her life.

It was nearly midnight when Panayota finally decided to respond to her cousin. Pursing her lips together, she whistled just loud enough to be heard by Aggelo above her.

She was tired of hiding. She was tired of keeping secrets.

CHAPTER 3:
MARRIED OR TARNISHED

LIKE EVERYTHING ELSE IN THE region, Kupaki sat on a hillside and was surrounded in every direction by more craggy hills and mountains as high as 9,000 feet. The village boasted no straight lines, no flat ground. Isolated in a picturesque landscape of rolling hills and rugged scrubland, a lonely outpost above the River Mornos, it was a world unto itself.

The two main cobble stone paths dissected the village like a cross, the lines converging at the main square in the middle of the village. The news and the gossip for the three hundred permanent residents, who supported themselves by farming and shepherding sheep or goats, were exchanged by the men mostly at the general village stores which stood around the village public square, and by the women at the water springs, the bigger of which was near the middle of the village and several smaller ones at the peripheral neighborhoods.

The most important public buildings were the church and school that stood next to each other at the lower part of the village, visible from nearly every house.

Kupaki was nearly inscrutable at night, a murky tableau of mystery and shadow, but in the light of day, the tiny village held no secrets. Everybody knew everybody and secrets, even intimate in nature were nearly impossible to be upheld. A stranger stood out and rumors spread like wildfire.

So it was that as Thanasis pondered his cousin's dilemma, he did so with her family, her neighbors, and the village itself in mind. The men in the family wanted to force George to marry Panayota, but the women thought she should absorb the shame of their illicit affair now and forget about the young man, who would most likely make her miserable for the rest of her life. Better to endure a few whispers and disapproving stares now, they said, than to marry a scoundrel. Common sense told Thanasis that the women were right, but his pride told him something else.

A few days later, when he spotted George walking near the village store, Thanasis hastened his steps to catch up with the young man. George had been avoiding him, but Thanasis was determined to confront him. He would try to make peace, but if no solution presented itself, he was prepared to show his teeth. "George," Thanasis said, "you know and I know what's happened with Panayota. I want you to honor your word."

Before George could reply, much less digest Thanasis's words, Metsios approached from the nearby vineyards. "Hi," he said as soon as he joined them.

George acknowledged Metsios and then turned to Thanasis. "There is nothing going on between me and Panayota. Do not listen to the village gossip."

"Leave that out," Thanasis snapped. "We know better."

Metsios spoke up. "George, I treated you as a friend, and you came near me and my home. At the end, you slept with my sister and blemished her honor. All the family is against me now. I'll give my sister seventy thousand drachmas as a dowry. I don't want you to feel you're marrying Metsios Soulias's sister without a dowry. I'll support my sister and be a very good brother to you."

George glanced away thoughtfully. "I need to think it over," he said. "I have sisters who aren't married yet. I want to be a good, protective brother and wait to marry until after they have married."

"What do you mean?" Thanasis retorted. "Some of your sisters are several years younger than you. Are you going to take decisions when they are of marriageable age?"

George looked like prey trying to squirm free from a predator's jaws. "I have no job. I might need to leave the village. I might have to go to America all together. I have not promised anything to Panayota, anyway."

Metsios's young, innocent-looking face darkened. "Why, you two-faced fuck..."

Thanasis, moving a step closer, locked eyes with George. "Listen, you had better honor your word to my cousin. I will not let that honor be lost to you. I will see that you forget all these excuses and think hard on solutions."

Thanasis could intimidate and even threaten George. Panayota, on the other hand, he had to treat far more gently.

He had always felt protective of his cousin, whose family, he felt, had already borne a great hardship. Georgios Soulias, Panayota's father, had died only a few years after crossing the Atlantic in search of his fortune, one among a million young Greek men to immigrate to America between 1910 and 1920. The father of two girls, Georgios had left determined to build a new life for his family. But unbeknownst to him, he had already created a new life, and that life was growing in his wife's womb. He never met his son. Metsios was just four years old when news arrived that his father, a phantom he only knew through stories, photos, and letters, had died in surgery, the victim of stomach troubles.

From that day on, the Soulias family had been forced to think about just one thing: survival. The fields they owned in the village produced barely enough food for the family, so, the eldest sister went to work for other villagers in their fields for daily wages. She also found work as a seamstress when no one needed her in the fields. Panayota hired on with the Koinis family, which looked after her like one of their own. Metsios, Paraskevi's baby, was doted on by his mother. If he got so much as an upset stomach, she teetered on the edge of panic. Understandably so, Thanasis thought, given how Georgios had died.

As the days wore on after Panayota's second virginity test, Thanasis spoke with her repeatedly, often for hours at a time, but she had a mind of her own.

"What about... ?"

Each time she began a sentence that way, Thanasis knew his cousin was about to invoke the name of some young man in the village who had gone from troublemaker to domesticated husband in a few short years.

"Was he a saint?" she would ask. "Was he not immature?"

She would then refer to specific incidents known by all in the village, incidents that revealed the young man's colorful past.

"Isn't he a good family man today?" she would ask.

Thanasis couldn't deny her logic, but at the same time he knew George belonged to a different breed. He was like a wild animal: cagey and unpredictable. Could anyone tame him? Even now, as the village buzzed with the rumors of his tawdry behavior, he regularly walked the path by the Koinis home, singing or whispering little love songs he had composed while Panayota was at work. Or he would stand on the balcony of his home, from where the Soulias house was visible, and, feigning innocence, invoke an old Greek tune:

*"Come to your window
And out of sight from your mom.
And pretend that you are watering
The pot with marjoram."*

Finally one day a solution presented itself. Thanasis was just leaving a cousin's home next door to the Nitsoses when Maria Nitsos, George's mother, called to him.

"Are you just going to stand there in the street, Thanasis?" she asked in a friendly voice. "Or would you like to come in and have a thimble of *ouzo* with Aunt Maria?"

Thanasis gladly accepted the invitation, and once inside, he only waited as long as politeness dictated before broaching the topic foremost on his mind.

"Aunt Maria," he began, pausing to take a sip of the sugary, anise-flavored aperitif George's mother had given him, "Your family and our family have always had good relations. I don't want to do anything to change that, but you should know what has happened between George and Panayota."

"I know," Maria said with a perceptive nod. "I know the whole story."

"Then you know what that means for a girl in our village," Thanasis replied. "My cousin is tarnished."

Maria frowned thoughtfully. "I know. I have girls myself, but listen, I don't want you and your family to worry. George is going to do the right thing by Panayota. He was always going to."

Thanasis cocked his head in surprise. He had no reason to doubt George's mother. If she was right, then Panayota's problem—the *family*'s problem—was solved at last.

CHAPTER 4:
OMEN

PANAYOTA SMILED TO HERSELF AS the little convoy crossed the River Mornos, still swollen from the spring rains. Just ahead of her were a couple of muleteers. Walking behind them with another mule was George Nitsos, her gallant fiancé, followed by several other muleteers.

Five years had passed since her cousin Thanasis had sat down to sip *ouzo* with Maria Nitsos, George's mother, and in that time, George and Panayota had enjoyed a long, uneventful engagement. True, they had never hosted an official engagement party, but they had nevertheless won the grudging approval of their families and village. Soon they would be wed at St. George's Church.

At the moment, with the noonday sun beating down on them, they were crossing the bridge over the River Mornos and inching closer to home. They had left a port by the sea earlier that morning, their dowry packed and loaded by mule drivers in anticipation of the slow trek back to Kupaki, which would cover more than twenty miles and take all day. Weighing down their procession of pack mules was an assortment of bedding, chests, silverware, plates, napkins, towels, and tablecloths—a remarkable haul purchased with their combined finances. Like any other young couple, they had relied on their family's wealth as well as their own meager resources, including Panayota's earnings from working for the Koinis family. Thanks to Panayota's savings, the Soulias dowry and the money sent from George's father in America, they'd been able to spend a princely sum, which in turn had earned them a bonus gift: a magnificent set of glassware from the store owner in the big city Patras. The gift, as dictated by custom, had been directly proportional to the amount of money they had spent. Unwilling to trust the beautiful glassware's fate to any of the muleteers, George had insisted on carrying it on the mule he was leading.

Panayota could see the future already. She and George would

entertain often, sharing their home and their bounty with the same people who had once threatened to chop her into pieces and toss her into the river. She would savor the delicious irony of her newfound domestic status as she poured each of her guests a refreshing drink from an exquisite glass pitcher. *"More water?"* she could imagine saying. *"It's fresh from the—"*

A terrible crash behind her—and the sound of George shouting in alarm—jolted her from her reverie. She turned to see him standing beside his mule and staring angrily at the ground, where the box containing the coveted glassware now lay on its side. Judging by the percussive sound generated by its impact, the glassware was in pieces.

"Fuck the fucking box and the fucking glassware!" a red-faced George said. His charming smile had disappeared, and his mischievous eyes were no longer dancing. "Fuck its father! Fuck its mother!"

Panayota covered her mouth with her hand. Should she laugh or cry? She wasn't sure. Finally she decided to open the box, just to see with her own eyes that indeed her lovely glassware was no more. But before she could take hold of the lid, George jerked her away.

"Just let the fucking thing lie there!" he snarled.

Panayota glanced from her fuming fiancé to the other muleteers, who were looking away in embarrassment. She felt a growing sense of foreboding. Was this to be her future? If so, it frightened her.

On June 2, 1940, as everyone gathered at St. George's Church, Thanasis glanced from pew to pew and saw that nearly the entire village had come to watch Papazois, the village priest, bless the union of George Nitsos and Panayota Soulias. Although he'd pushed George to do the right thing by Panayota, Thanasis sometimes wondered if the women in the family had been wiser: maybe he should have let the scoundrel off the hook. Dressed in his best suit and wearing a look of self-satisfaction, the lean groom looked like the proverbial cat that had just swallowed the canary.

A man in his shoes should exercise more humility, Thanasis thought.

After all, George Nitsos was about to commit his life to another soul in front of God and everyone he knew. Thanasis knew from experience that such a commitment could not be rushed into—or taken lightly. He himself was engaged now to Polyxeni Gumas, a good friend and former classmate of Panayota's. Their engagement, he reflected, was the result of patience and negotiation, not hubris.

A year earlier, while still an eligible bachelor, Thanasis had been approached by the village store owner and Polyxeni's uncle, who had suggested that Thanasis consider marrying his niece. Negotiations, however, had quickly broken down when Panokostas, Thanasis's father, began insisting on a larger dowry than the Gumas family could provide. Panayota became one of Polyxeni's most vocal proponents, citing the girl's beauty, work ethic, and academic achievement. "She herself is the dowry," Panayota told Thanasis. Panokostas continued to insist on a more substantial dowry. It wasn't long before he had earned the nickname of "Dowry Konandreas," as well as the moniker, "Gave dowry, will have dowry," which was often chanted by the younger generation of Gumases as soon as he was out of earshot and followed by howls of mirth.

There was also the matter of Thanasis's reputation—and Polyxeni's view of him. He had made a lousy impression, years earlier, when he had beaten up another man and the news had reached his father— and Polyxeni and her family—while the group had been talking at a market in a nearby town. Worse, there was his thundering voice. He was loud. His whole family was loud. They had to be in order to communicate out in the fields. But such rough edges weren't exactly a selling point when it came to seeking out a potential bride.

Thanasis's sisters and their husbands had told him that Polyxeni was a very nice young maiden, but since each husband's family had received a hefty dowry from the Konandreases, they had hesitated to say a dowry shouldn't be an issue. Panayota, though, had possessed no dowry when she had been courted by George. She had acted on her own and in fact had disregarded many village and family biases. Thus, when Thanasis had all but given up on the idea of marrying Polyxeni, Panayota had reminded him privately that it was *his* decision to get married, not his father's. Thanasis had countered that he didn't want to disregard his parents' opinions, at which point his cousin had cleverly pointed out that his father only disapproved of the dowry, not the girl. Marrying Polyxeni would not be the same thing as disregarding his father's wishes. Thanasis had finally presented the argument to his parents in simple terms: "Polyxeni is better than a thousand dowries." Panokostas, impressed by his son's earnest plea, had capitulated.

Thanasis glanced from George Nitsos, still looking smug at the altar, to his fiancée. Indeed, Polyxeni Gumas was worth more than any dowry. One of the most beautiful women inside the church, she exuded equal parts dignity and calm. She was a force to be reckoned with, and he could hardly wait for their turn at the altar.

He got it two months later when, on August 23, 1940, they exchanged their own wedding vows. Soon after, Panokostas was singing the praises of his new daughter-in-law, who was hard-working, obedient, and gentle. In fact, it seemed there were few qualities that Polyxeni did not possess when Panokostas boasted about her to anyone who cared to listen. He extolled her virtues with the same passion he had employed while arguing against the marriage.

CHAPTER 5:
DARK DAYS

By October of 1940, the hills surrounding Kupaki were aflame in autumnal shades of red, silver, yellow, and green. Chrysanthemums, geraniums, and quince fruit adorned front yards, balconies, and gardens.

That was the last Thanasis would see of his village or its blooms until the following year. Greece, bullied and provoked by Italy, was about to enter World War II. Thanasis would be among Kupaki's thirty-five young men, including George Nitsos, to leave the village and join the fighting in the mountains to the north. The lesser equipped Greek army trounced the Italians, but when Hitler sent his elite units to attack Greece on several fronts, everything changed. The Greeks put up a heroic resistance but were eventually forced to surrender.

Soon the Italians came and occupied Kupaki, to Thanasis bewilderment. How had it come to pass, he wondered, that the enemy they had so soundly beaten on the battlefield was now their conqueror? Just months earlier, Thanasis, aided by a handful of fellow Greek soldiers, had escorted thousands of Italian prisoners of war to the Greek interior. Now he and his fellow countrymen were the vanquished.

The occupation thus entered its darkest days, with the Germans confiscating food supplies in Greece to use for their own soldiers and allies, as well as their expedition to Africa. The occupants also enforced a blockade, preventing food from being imported or even shipped from one part of Greece, where it was produced, to another. Locally, several villagers died from malnutrition and poor medical care. The Konandreas and Gumas families, like most in Kupaki, endured their share of misfortune. By the end of 1943, Thanasis and Polyxeni had each lost their father.

The blockade forced many families to move from the big cities to the countryside in order to find enough food to survive. The poor mountainous villages around Kupaki were now witnessing an influx of arrivals, many of whom had not been seen in the villages for decades. These young returnees were direct descendants of the Galatades, the shepherds who since 1920 had been undertaking an annual winter sojourn to Athens. Each family would herd its flock in October and walk for seventeen days straight, all the way to Athens. Once in the capital city, they would settle on the foothills around the city, sleeping in primitive shacks. During the day, they would sell milk and other dairy products in nearby Kolonaki and to the parliamentary elite Athenians. Then, in early spring, they would walk back to the village. The Galatades' exposure to such privileged Athenians taught them how to appreciate the finer things in life, things they didn't have: education, sophistication, and material possessions such as nice clothing and jewelry. Along with their milk money, they brought back to the village new customs and styles of dress, openly flaunting them.

George Nitsos was ecstatic to see all the young people return, and soon he was interacting with them on a daily basis.

"They are wearing better clothes," Thanasis told Polyxeni one day, "but did you notice how emaciated they look?"

"Makes your heart hurt, doesn't it?" Polyxeni responded.

Frail or not, soon all the newcomers were at work plowing, digging, and planting, and most bought or had been given by the locals a goat or two for their milk.

The Italians encamped beside the remains of the bridge over the River Mornos. The bridge had been destroyed by Greek resistance fighters with the aid of the British, and the Italians often walked into Kupaki on foot in search of provisions. The villagers had no choice but to open their larders and give them whatever they could: chestnuts, walnuts, feta cheese, and wine. Sometimes they even had to give away precious chickens or other livestock. The occupiers might offer in return a pack of Italian cigarettes wrapped in shiny saran, uttering the phrase, "*Una faccia, una razza,*" which meant, "Same face, same race."

Surprisingly, George Nitsos, no longer able to depend on checks from his father in America due to the blockade, had embraced hard work in order to survive. Many in Kupaki had been amazed to see him plowing his field and planting seeds, but in his usual fashion, George, a born politician, was also carving out more influence in the village and among the Italians. As the new village warden, he was now in regular close contact with the occupiers. In fact, he was helping them to gather provisions from people's homes. When two resistance Greek groups were formed, one leaning politically to the right and the other to the left, George found a way to placate both sides. This made many in the village—including Thanasis—agree not to entrust George with information vital to the resistance.

In 1943, when the Italians capitulated and the Germans took over, George tried to befriend them. He had no luck. In contrast with their Latin allies, the Germans treated his efforts at approaching them with chilly suspicion.

Because the Germans had a reputation for arresting and sometimes indiscriminately shooting villagers found near any damage done by the resistance fighters, a meeting was called at the village. It was well known and practiced in the area that small villages who had only limited firepower should avoid provoking the Germans, and in addition should send them cheese, eggs, fruit, and wine. It was decided that George, Panaitakis, and Thanasis, all three owners of property near the Germans' encampment and therefore in danger, would walk together to the camp to present the village's peace offering. When the time came to carry out their mission, Thanasis and Panaitakis waited in vain for George, who never appeared. Concerned that someone might attempt something rash, like sabotage, the two men went alone and presented their gift to the Germans.

Later, George offered a curious explanation for his absence. "I saw you going and followed you," he told Thanasis. "I hate the Germans so much I was thinking of throwing a hand grenade and blowing them up."

If George and others lusted for German blood, few had the temerity to draw any. Instead, it was the occupiers who did most of the bloodletting. Only weeks after George's threats to blow up the occupiers, the Germans hanged from a tree two young men who hailed from a nearby village. Their crime? Some farmers from another village had cut a section of the Germans' telephone lines in order to tie a plow and yoke together.

See Dramatis Personae at end of book.

CHAPTER 6:
KOLITO

MORE THAN A YEAR HAD passed since the youth had arrived in Kupaki from Athens. The old-timers had had time to appreciate the educational opportunities the big city had given to the newcomers, but they were less impressed by their urban moral codes which were looser and more individualistic. Kupaki, isolated for so many years by its rugged hills and remote location, struggled to hold back the tides of modernization.

Thanasis, by now approaching middle age, shared the old-timers' general opinion of the young returnees, but he was more concerned about George Nitsos, the man he had pressured to marry his cousin. Thanasis expected George to work hard to support Panayota, but George was still spending carefree days with his bachelor friends, ecstatically joining them in all their activities.

Thanasis learned that the youth of the village, organized by the newcomers, had joined a youth resistance movement and had prepared a theatrical performance with resistance themes. A dance followed in the open behind the altar at St. George and was enjoyed by all.

A few days later, Thanasis was returning with Polyxeni from their field one night when he noticed several people looking from the street into the school's big hall. He stopped his horse and could hear the voices of George Nitsos and Tsipropanos from inside the big hall.

"What is it?" Polyxeni asked.

Two main paths converged behind the school hall, and others had stopped as well to take in the spectacle. Farmers and shepherds, tired from working all day in the fields, paused alongside their horses and mules. Some of the older men and women on hand were crossing themselves in disbelief. Others were shaking their heads in disapproval.

Polyxeni gulped. "Are they ... *dancing?*"

Thanasis raised an eyebrow. "I'm not sure I'd call that dancing."

"Who is teaching them this thing?" Polyxeni asked.

Thanasis, unsure, shrugged his shoulders.

"They have a dance instructor," answered a young bystander, who appeared knowledgeable on the subject. "Your cousin Tsipropanos knows him and brought him here to teach."

"Oh, crazy Tsipropanos," Polyxeni murmured.

A conversation ensued between Thanasis, Polyxeni, the young bystander, and several others, and Thanasis was slowly brought up to speed on the dancing. The instructor was Nick, who hailed from a village north of Kupaki. He had learned the European dances at a studio in Athens, dancing in the evenings after working all day. To most congregating outside the school hall, Nick was a stranger and an outsider who had left his village and his work in his fields and come to Kupaki to teach a new dance. Tsipropanos, Polyxeni's cousin and a young theology student, had recently returned to Kupaki from the University of Athens. After the theater dance, he had realized that the youth in his village were out of step with their cosmopolitan counterparts and had asked Nick, whom he knew, to come to the village, stay at his place, and bring the latest European dance to Kupaki.

"Is he doing it for free?" Polyxeni asked.

Money, thanks to the war, was no longer worth anything, and people bartered for what they wanted.

"The students will pay him in wheat," the same young man answered.

At the sound of the word *wheat*, many crossed themselves. Money was worth nothing, but wheat was precious.

For his part, Thanasi wanted nothing to do with the madness. He was old enough to know that such frivolity rubbed the villagers the wrong way. Their country was occupied. Their people were starving, and the youth wanted to dance and pay with wheat?

The next evening, Thanasis spotted more curious villagers gathered around the school. A gramophone inside was blaring a tune completely different from the traditional regional melodies.

Thanasis had learned the latest gossip about the dancing from his wife's siblings, three of whom were in the class. They had argued with their mother, Aggeliki, by saying that the dance had attracted almost forty students and that there was nothing wrong with it. They had pointed out that it was their cousin Tsipropanos who had organized it, and had himself brought Nick to the village.

Aggeliki had already expressed her frustration directly to Tsipropanos, the young theology student, for his role in what to her was a scandal. "You left the village for Athens to study God," she told her nephew Tsipropanos, "and you brought the devil back with you." The devil, of course, was Nick, the dance instructor.

The village's youth had argued that it wasn't just young people participating; some married couples, like George and Panayota, were attending the classes, as well. George, in fact, was urging everybody to participate. With even married couples joining in, Thanasis was now convinced, no one could stop the dancing. Life would go on, with or without money, with or without enough food on the table. The youth of the village would see to that. What Thanasis couldn't understand was what George and Panayota were doing there?

At half past four every afternoon, young men and women abandoned their work in droves. Their parents would take over for them while they rushed home to change. On their way home, the girls would stop at the springs to wash their hands, feet, and armpits. The more enterprising among them would perfume themselves with basil leaves from their gardens or a rose from the school's flower garden, mashing the plants into a pulp in their hands and rubbing the paste into their armpits or around their necks.

Like the others in attendance, George and Panayota had paid the price of admission, which was good for the summer: two *okas* (ten pounds) of wheat for her and three *okas* (fifteen pounds) for him. The dance, meanwhile, was like nothing anyone had ever seen. The older generation didn't even bother to learn how to pronounce—much less differentiate between—the new dances. Whether it was a tango, waltz, or fox trot, the old-timers dismissively called it *Kolito*, or fusion, since it hardly resembled traditional Greek line dancing. The new dances, which paired couples in close proximity, came to be synonymous with sinfulness and licentiousness. Men and women held hands and moved closely together, simultaneously insulting common morals, culture, and tradition. Parents, grandparents, and other elders in town were incredulous that the youth in the village were so willing to give away good wheat during a near famine just to hoof it around the hall, but their protests were to no avail.

A few days after the first dance lesson, Thanasis and Polyxeni met Panayota outside the school hall.

"You're such a good dancer, cousin," Thanasis said disapprovingly. "These lessons are a waste for you. It's time you concentrate on other things that need attention, like having children."

Panayota offered a self-deprecating smile. "Oh, Thanasis, you know what a big baby George is. I'm not sure I could handle having another child in the family."

Thanasis laughed politely.

"Anyway," Panayota continued, "George needs my company here. I have to keep an eye on him, don't I? One of the graceful young things inside might have designs on my husband." She broke into a peal of laughter that belied the dangerous truth in her words.

Thanasis shook his head glumly. When Panayota made up her mind to do something, there was no dissuading her.

The dancing sessions ran late each night, and Panayota was surprised one evening when the old hand-wound clock on the school wall struck ten. The dancers were illuminated by a flickering kerosene lamp, which cast long shadows of figures on the walls. Beyond the windows, shapes could be spied in the darkness outside, where parents waiting to escort their children home stood alongside curious onlookers. Many were moving to the music. They would be fresh converts for Nick, Panayota mused.

Inside the hall, Panayota noticed her husband dancing with a buxom young girl whose flushed cheeks were doing nothing to dissuade her partner from calling out endearments to her. Such behavior wasn't new for George, who regularly began the night dancing with cousins before moving on to other young ladies not related to him by blood. His vulgar flirtations invariably embarrassed the girls, but he always had a ready excuse for treating them so familiarly.

"Now, George, please!" the girl said, pushing his hand away when he squeezed her and bent over as if to kiss her.

George feigned innocence. "Come on now. We're like family. My great-uncle's sister-in-law was your father's ..."

Panayota leaned against the back wall and tried her best not to acknowledge her husband's shameful conduct. It was going to be another long night.

The song came to an end, and Nick reached for the needle to remove it from the record, which was still spinning.

George, ever impetuous, availed himself of the brief lull. "Any of you young guys want to take my wife?" he asked, laughing. "It won't be for nothing. I will make sure she comes with a good dowry."

The room fell silent, and, judging by the look on George's face, he quickly understood that he had gone too far.

Panayota glanced around the room nervously. "Don't worry, George," she said, flashing a smile. "You won't have to give anybody a dowry. All these young men know what a lady like me is worth. They'll be happy to have me for nothing."

George, clearly hoping to make amends for his crude remark, was quick to reply. "Don't I know that, my sweet?" he said in the sugary voice that so many women in the village seemed to find irresistible. "Looks like you're the only one here that knows I was joking. Look at all their faces! Do you all really think I would give up my darling wife? Not for a million drachmas! Not for the whole world!"

A few days later, George sat down with the dance instructor to enjoy a glass of *ouzo*. George couldn't help relishing the fact that someone else—Nick in this case—was bearing the brunt of the village's scorn. Several elders regularly cursed Nick and prayed for the day he would leave the village and never come back. They complained that never before had young unmarried men and women been in such close proximity to each other, which could only lead to trouble. They complained that the young people not only spent precious time and wheat on learning to dance but had also begun practicing dance steps while working in the fields.

"Do you know that you and I are not just spreading licentiousness in Kupaki?" George quipped. "We're also to blame for bad crops and lost sheep."

Nick laughed quietly as he sipped at his *ouzo*.

The dance lessons had become the talk of the village. Who was carrying on with whom? Who smelled strongly of basil and sweat? Whose wheat was justifiably spent? And whose was simply wasted because he had two left feet?

Panayota came to dread dance lessons. There was no telling who George was going to flirt with or what he was going to say on any given night. How would he embarrass her next? By now, many were openly gossiping about his designs on Poly, a pretty young girl who showed up each night at the dance hall. He was dancing with her over and over, whispering in her ear. His demeanor was showing utmost infatuation, but because Panayota was there and Poly was the granddaughter of his godfather, few suspected George's true intentions toward Poly.

The afternoon of August 29, 1944, Panayota's worries were overshadowed by the occupation as she watched in disbelief plumes of roiling black smoke rising in the east over the hill of St. Nicholas. The Germans, determined to punish the resistance for an ambush earlier in the month near the county's capital Lidoriki, burned the town to the ground.

The other villagers who had arrived for the nightly dance lesson searched the horizon nervously. Several turned and started for home, disappearing behind the stately cypress and poplar trees that lined the schoolyard.

George remained defiant. He strode into the school hall and began turning the crank on the gramophone. "Let's have one more glass!" he called out to the others. "One more red one!"

Kakia Mendris's popular song extolling the pleasures of "one more glass, one more song" blared jovially from the gramophone: *"Akoma ena potiraki, Akoma ena tragudaki ..."*

"Come on, everybody!" George continued. "Cheer up! If we're all going to die, we might as well die dancing!"

The next morning, Kupaki did its part when the leftists called on the surrounding villages for help. Several horses and mules were loaded with food, supplies, and blankets and sent from the village to the capital.

Panayota did not know then how close Kupaki and the next villages were to such retaliation by the Germans. It came to light later. At Krokylion, the village less than three miles from Kupaki, the leftists were hiding Elias Barzelai, the chief Rabbi of the Jewish Community of Athens, along with his wife and teenage daughter. And at Zoriano, the village less than two miles from Kupaki, all the records with the names of all the Jews of Athens were hidden. Information of this sort would have brought the Germans, torches and guns in hand.

The dance lessons, meanwhile, came to an end a few days later. Nick had managed to amass one hundred and seventy *okas* of wheat, enough to feed a family of four frugally for nearly six months. He loaded the sacks onto two horses and set off, stopping at a villager's house on the way out of the village to return the gramophone he had borrowed, along with seventeen *okas* of wheat as payment.

Kupaki's youth missed him before he even disappeared from view. Even some adults who had vehemently criticized him lamented his departure. "For all his prancing and turning the heads of our children," some said, "that lad wasn't so bad, after all."

Panayota, too, was sad to see him leave, but she also felt a sense of relief. The nightly roulette with George and his crude remarks from the center of the school hall—for everyone to hear—was over.

CHAPTER 7:
FLIRTING

It wasn't long before Panayota's public humiliation was old news, for the villagers soon had something new to talk about: the German occupiers were packing up their trucks and leaving. The locals reacted by cursing the withdrawing Germans within earshot. Those who had lost loved ones to the fighting were especially vocal.

While the Germans headed for the exit, one man, now a hero, was rumored to be returning. Nick, it was said, was planning to marry one of his ex-students. The village buzzed with anticipation. Soon Nick and his young bride would be elegantly performing the Dance of Isaiah, a much venerated ritual at any Greek Orthodox wedding, at St. George Church.

Along with the news about Nick's plans, another rumor was spreading in the village about George's latest infatuation: Poly, granddaughter of George's godfather. Though the dancing at the school's hall was over, he was wasting no opportunity to besiege her, and there were plenty of opportunities.

The weather during the harvest in the autumn of 1944 was glorious, with one sunny day following another. The grain and grape harvests, the husking, the wine and syrup making, the fruit picking—all were occasions for merrymaking, courtship, and dancing with the gramophone music. During the dancing, many times in the open with the villagers looking on, George had been seen whispering endearments to Poly with impunity.

Panayota tried to tell herself that even George would not be so godless as to taint a relationship by baptism, but she could see that he was becoming bolder still.

In the days that followed, the rumors continued to spread, with each one eventually finding its way to Panayota's ears. George was passing messages to Poly now. He was rendezvousing with her outside the village in remote places where they had no earthly reason to meet.

Panayota briefly considered confronting her husband. After all, she knew his pattern all too well. This was how he had courted her not so long ago—secretly, unsavorily, and without the village's approval. If she confronted him, she knew he would simply go on the offensive. He would pretend to be shocked.

She could see his reaction now:

"How could you even consider the possibility of such a relationship?"

Perhaps, had George possessed a better work ethic, he would have been too busy for such dalliances. After the Germans left and Greece was officially liberated, the country undertook a great rebuilding effort with the help of foreign aid. Suddenly American dollars were pouring into the country. George, who quit his job as the village warden as soon as his father began sending money again, boasted to anyone who would listen about his sudden influx of wealth. Much of that money was spent on his wardrobe, which he carefully cultivated as part of his urban veneer. Always dressed to the nines, he spent most of his time loafing about in the village square, where he endeavored to impress his fellow villagers with card tricks and the streetwise language he had adopted during his youthful days in the big city of Patras.

Greece had hardly celebrated the ouster of the Germans—indeed, at the Acropolis in Athens the German flag had hardly been lowered and the white-on-blue cross of the Greek flag raised—when old rivalries between Nationalists and Communists began once again to smolder. The Greek citizens saw only the dark outlines of the columns of the Parthenon, not the sun's bright rays filtering through. The Nationalists had the support of the British and later the Americans. The Communists, meanwhile, were backed by the Russians and other Eastern European republics. Then there were the Socialists, whose ideology fell somewhere between the two extremes.

The tug of war between the various factions could be felt even in remote Kupaki, and by the spring of 1946, armed units from both groups began visiting the village.

Sensing danger, the men in Kupaki had another meeting to discuss the safety of their families.

Some men, who were leftists, pledged to protect the village from the Communists.

George joined them. "I will help, too," he said in a magnanimous tone.

When others pledged to protect the village from the Nationalists, George once again pledged his help, this time with the Nationalists.

But in the ensuing days and weeks, it wasn't clear whose side George was on, much less who, if anybody, he had the power to protect. While in the company of Communists, he extolled the efforts of his "comrades" to save the country and bring about equality, but while chewing the fat with the Nationalists, he declared himself their man, a capitalist whose family was sending him money from America. To prove the point, he would produce a handful of American dollars and order a round of *ouzo* for his fellow citizens of the free world.

The pressure to do something—anything—to stop George from continuing his pursuit of Poly reached a fever pitch one day when Thanasis was approached by Mary, the wife of a poor shepherd, while at his fields in Maraveli.

"Linatsas," she said, using George's nickname, "told me he's planning to divorce Panayota so he can marry Poly."

Thanasis felt his blood boil. He had already discussed the issue with Polyxeni, Aggelo, and his other sister Papadia, who had insisted that he take the matter to Poly's father. Aggelo, in fact, had already approached Panayota, who had denied the rumors and attributed them to malicious gossip. Thanasis had at first resisted the idea of confronting Poly's father, who was his cousin, after all.

Yet here was Mary, not known as a gossip, confirming what everyone suspected. How could he not get involved?

Thanasis thanked Mary for her candor and then marched straight to his cousin's house.

"I knew George was after my daughter," Poly's father said in an alarmed tone after Thanasis told him what George was doing, "but I had no idea he was actually planning on divorcing Panayota. I'm going to have a long talk with Poly."

A few weeks later, Thanasis met again with Poly's father after it had become apparent that his talk had not produced the desired results. George was still inventing ways to get close to her.

"I will either have to leave the village with her," Poly's father said, "or kill the bastard."

Thanasis raised a hand in protest. "Don't even think such things," he said, remembering a time not so long in the past when he had spent time in jail after losing his temper.

Thanasis breathed a sigh of relief that summer when George received a government appointment to a city farther north in Greece. There he was to receive military training along with many others and, if judged fit, to be utilized by the Nationalists in the war against the Communists. Despite his best efforts to play both sides, George Nitsos had been forced to come down squarely on the side of the Nationalists. Whether or not he would be able to maintain loyalty to anyone but himself was a matter very much open to debate.

CHAPTER 8:
SHINING STAR OF THE SKY

PANAYOTA WAS WALKING A WINDING cobblestone path near her home one sunny morning in early September 1946 when she heard a familiar echo. Kantas, the mailman, was announcing his arrival in Kupaki by blowing his curved brass horn. Judging by the percussive rebound of the proclamation as it sliced its way along the village's narrow footpaths, Kantas was almost to the village square. Although he only came to Kupaki two or three times each week, usually around ten o'clock in the morning, he almost always had something for Panayota, who regularly received letters from her various family members in America, New Zealand, Australia, and, closer to home, Athens. These days, she could also count on a letter from George each week now that he was away.

Today Panayota didn't have her own mail in mind. Her hands tingled with dread and her heart raced as she scurried down the path. She reached the village square just as several others were converging on it from other village paths.

Ahead was Kantas, horn still in hand, bulging leather bag slung over his shoulder. As a growing crowd began to gather around the frail, thin man, he climbed the stone steps from the main square to the front of the village store, his final destination. Kantas, assuming an air of importance, placed his leather bag on a metal tripod table and sat on a chair beside it. He seemed pleased that so many had assembled around him.

Indeed, Panayota noted there were more on hand than usual, most likely because of the summer vacation.

Kantas was slowly and deliberately removing various items from the many compartments in his leather bag: stamps, a fountain pen, a small bottle of ink, wax to seal envelopes, his old wrinkled logbook, and finally the mail itself. He was obviously savoring each moment, basking in his importance, as the circle of villagers around him drew closer.

She took up a position directly behind Kantas so she could gaze over his bony left shoulder as he began reading out the names on the envelopes and packages.

It was all Panayota could do to quell the impatience welling inside her. She watched intently as he began to call out the names of each recipient one letter at a time. When she spied the name she had been looking for, she snatched the letter from Kantas before he could read for himself the name on the envelope, much less announce it to the assembled crowd.

A speechless Kantas jerked around in surprise.

"I'll deliver that for you," Panayota said breezily. "It's for my husband's cousin. He's still in his fields and has asked me to collect his mail."

Kantas nodded his assent, although a look of surprise still showed on his face. He might have protested, Panayota thought, if she had ever given him a reason to suspect her motives. She had only had honest dealings with Kantas. Moreover, in such a close-knit community, it was quite common, even necessary, for the postman to allow villagers to pass on letters to their friends and family.

With the letter safely tucked beneath her arm, Panayota hurried across the slate-covered yard of the store and disappeared around the corner. Once out of sight, she continued halfway home and then stopped where the path curved between houses. With shaking hands she tore the letter from the envelope. As her eyes raced down the page, she unconsciously formed each word with her lips. By the time she had finished the letter, she was blind with rage.

She jerked around violently and stormed back the way she had come.

Seconds later, she was back on the path next to the store. Kantas, still seated beside the metal table, was placidly licking stamps for the outgoing mail while sipping *ouzo* offered by one of the villagers, probably someone who had just received good news. Panayota marched straight past him and stopped in the middle of the village square facing the Poly's house. In the middle of the square and in front of dozens of her fellow villagers, a panting and furious Panayota vented her spleen.

"Come out, you!" she called toward Poly's house. "Come out and hear what your darling has written to you!"

As she began to read from the letter in her trembling hand, Panayota barely noticed the others in the square, the store, the balconies, and the paths who had collectively stopped whatever they had been doing—reading, making small talk, relaxing in the shade—to stare at her.

"*My very beloved Poly, shining star of the sky...*" Panayota's voice was choked with fury.

The letter she had stolen wasn't addressed to George's cousin, of course. It was for Poly—and had been written by George.

Kantas leapt to his feet, nearly stumbling in the process, *ouzo* trickling down the side of his mouth, and rushed down the stone steps. "Stop!" he called out to Panayota as he waved his arms wildly. "Stop reading! I'm going to lose my job! I'm going to lose my job!"

His small, squeaky voice was no match for Panayota's full-throated recitation of her husband's amorous dispatch to Poly. She continued reading the letter aloud for all to hear until finally, exhausted from her exertions, she suddenly became aware of Kantas, who was still pleading with her to stop, as well as the crowd of onlookers. Panayota felt her cheeks pale. What had she done? To steal someone else's mail, to possibly jeopardize an innocent man's job—this was not like her.

"I'm sorry, Kantas," she said softly. She then raised her voice so her audience could hear. "Mr. Kantas here has done nothing wrong. If it ever comes to him losing his job, I will own up to my responsibility and tell any official that will listen that I snatched this letter from his hands and ran away."

A few short days later, Poly's father left the village with his daughter in tow. His dark prediction—that he might someday have to leave his home in order to preserve his family's honor—had come to fruition much sooner than anyone could have anticipated. Most in the village voiced compassion for Panayota, but their sympathetic words were invariably tinged with reproach for her behavior, which they claimed had been unbefitting a lady.

"Would you rather she wept in secret?" Thanasis asked anyone who dared criticize his cousin's actions. "Then how would you have known what that bastard Linatsas was doing to her?"

Thanasis was proud of his cousin's spirit, although he feared for her safety. How would that cowardly philanderer react when news reached him that Poly had been whisked away by her father after Panayota had aired their dirty secrets for all to hear? Panayota would never leave George; she was too honorable, but what about him? Would he find a way to pay her back for standing up to him?

CHAPTER 9:
DEAD SERIOUS

"PANAITAKIS, ARE YOU SURE YOU both heard right?" Thanasis wasn't sure which emotion to indulge first: anger or disbelief.

"Which part of George Nitsos offering us money to kill Panayota could we have heard wrong?" Panaitakis replied.

"I might be a bit hard of hearing," his wife Mary added, "but I heard it very well—and many times, indeed."

Only a handful of days had passed since Panayota's furious recitation in the village square. The sultry summer weather of 1946 was still hanging on, although the September days were growing shorter. At the moment, Thanasis was standing on the second floor of the Konandreas hut, a rustic building in the middle of the family's fields in Maraveli, just outside of Kupaki. Hay and other livestock supplies were stored on the first floor, while the second level, an open space, was meant for human habitation. A fireplace occupied the far wall and sat opposite the east-facing balcony.

Across from Thanasis stood Panaitakis and Mary. Panaitakis, a hardy peasant farmer barely five feet, four inches tall, was illiterate but an accomplished cooper and the owner of a keen, philosophical mind. He was always on the lookout for how things worked and how nature functioned. His wife was perhaps an inch shorter. Lean, hard of hearing, she, too, was illiterate but sharp. Together, they had just made an explosive allegation: George Nitsos, before leaving for military training, had not once but several times offered to pay them to kill Panayota.

The Panaitakis and Mary worked on George's fields as crop partners and were dependent on him for their livelihood. They were simple, hardworking, God-fearing people with no reason to lie. Still, their story struck Thanasis as incredible.

"Tell me again how he approached you," he said.

"We thought he was joking at first," Mary explained. "He asked us if we would help kill Panayota. He said she had some illness in her womb that meant she could never have children. We said she looked well enough to us, and even if she was ill, surely modern doctors could cure her. We told him she's still young and can get better and have children."

"That's when he said he wanted to get rid of her so he could marry Poly," Panaitakis said. "He talked like he was joking, but we could tell he was dead serious."

"How exactly did he want you to do it?" Thanasis asked.

"He wanted me to call her from outside the house," Panaitakis said, "and throw a hand grenade at her when she came out. Nitsos said that everybody would think that she was just at the wrong place at the wrong time when the guerillas and the royalists were throwing grenades at each other."

As he listened to his explanation, Thanasis wondered why Panaitakis and his wife had waited so long to tell him about George's plans. But then it dawned on him: it was possible they had kept the conspiracy a secret from him for precisely the same reason he was currently doubting his own resolve to tell anyone else: no one would believe it.

"I managed to get out of it by saying that I had no idea how to use a grenade," Panaitakis continued. "He offered to teach me, but I said that I was too old a dog to learn new tricks. Another day, he came early one morning to Maraveli and said that he had arranged things so that Panayota would be riding to meet him there later that day and we should surprise her horse when she arrived at that steep part of the path where there's an eighty-foot drop on one side. He said she would fall all the way to the bottom head-first."

"And how did you get out of that one?"

"He was there, too, hiding behind a rock with Mary's kerchief covering his head so his wife wouldn't recognize him even if she saw him. When Panayota appeared about a hundred yards away, I told him that I could hear people coming in the opposite direction. He just leapt up and ran away before she got too close."

Thanasis frowned in disgust. "I can't believe that," he muttered.

Panaitakis wasn't finished. "He offered us money, clothing, a house to live in, livestock—you name it. He even talked about pushing her from an oak tree so that the fall would kill her."

"I'll have to talk to Panayota about this," Thanasis said, thinking aloud. He began to pace the wide plank flooring.

"I already did," Mary said sheepishly.

"What?" Thanasis couldn't believe his ears. "What else have you been hiding from me?"

Panaitakis nervously eyed the bare ceiling joists above them before returning Thanasis's gaze. "There was another time," he finally said, "when Nitsos asked me to help his cousin kill Panayota when she would be on her way to their fields. I went to see her before she was going to depart with my heart in my mouth. I told her not to go to her fields, and I pleaded with her not to talk to her husband about it and get me in trouble."

"And how did she react?"

"She burst into tears," he said, "and I consoled her, telling her that nobody would blame her if she divorced him, because we all know how he treats her. After a while, she dried her tears and made me promise not to tell anyone else in return for her not telling her husband what I'd told her."

"And she still hasn't divorced him!" Thanasis said in wonder.

Mary shrugged. "She told me, 'Don't talk to me about divorce, Mary. I would rather be dead than be the only divorced woman in the village.' And she asked me to leave before Nitsos returned."

"You do realize, don't you," Thanasis said to the old couple, "that I can't just let this go. I'll have to talk to Panayota, and she will know you told me."

They nodded.

"We are not among those people with loose tongues," Mary said. "But if it saves that poor woman's life, may the good Lord forgive us for talking to you against her wishes, even if she herself does not."

"Amen," Panaitakis said. "Please be careful. If Nitsos finds out, we won't have a roof over our heads, and we may be the ones lying dead in a ravine somewhere."

Thanasis's mind raced after the peasant couple left. If George had truly asked such a thing of the Panaitakis and Mary, it was only because he felt confident they were too dependent on him for work to ever go against him. As poor as they were, perhaps he thought they would do his bidding—if the price was right. By speaking almost in jest, he could always claim he was joking, should things go awry.

Thanasis briefly contemplated confronting George, but he knew the man would simply deny the whole conversation. Where, he would ask, was the proof? And why would he entrust the job of killing his wife to Panaitakis and Mary when he could do it himself and make it look like an accident? An innocent smile would creep across his face as he feigned indignation to his fellow villagers.

If the village store was the place where men traded gossip, the women did their talking at the village spring. There, under the cool greenery, the women of Kupaki exchanged the latest rumors, their voices masked by the sound of water trickling into barrels, pails, and pots. Mary traveled to the spring and discretely extended the circle of people privy to the murderous machinations of George Nitsos, who, she fretted, planned to kill Panayota after he returned from his training—and then blame Panaitakis and Mary.

Panayota caught wind of the rumor soon after it began to spread. Then she heard it directly from her cousin Thanasis, who approached her with the news one day beneath the shade of a scraggly old oak tree in the fields in Maraveli.

Thanasis, ever protective, was staring angrily at Panayota as he waited for a response.

"Don't look at me like that, Thanasis," she said. "You ask me why I didn't tell you. *This* is why. You look like you could kill now, and it doesn't make me feel better to know it's not me you want to kill but my husband. I don't want to be a widow any more than I want to be divorced. I still love George, you know. And I don't want you to go to jail for me by doing something stupid."

Thanasis's face softened. "I'm older now—and the father of four children. I'm not about to do anything insane and leave them orphans, much as I wish I could have it out with Nitsos. But I care about you. I want to protect you and do the best for your happiness and your safety. And frankly, I'm disappointed. I stood against half the village to get Nitsos to marry you. I threatened him when he seemed to be pulling out. Speaking of that, I don't remember you ever worrying about my temper back then. Now for your sake again, I'm asking you to leave that good-for-nothing criminal. I'd rather see you divorced than see you dead."

Panayota smiled ruefully. Part of her was angry at Thanasis for once again insinuating himself in her affairs, but she knew he did so out of genuine love. He had always been protective of her. Likewise, she had for years nurtured an almost maternal feeling toward him, despite being eight years his junior. There was a child inside dear Thanasis, the gallant protector of women. Yet he had no clue about the inner life of women—or his own softer feelings. During his courtship of Polyxeni, Panayota had often scolded and advised him with all the freedom of an elder sister, and though he had always pretended to merely be humoring her, she knew by his actions that he had always valued her opinion and had taken her advice seriously. Now, though, she wondered if there was a way to soothe his anger while politely asking him to stand down.

"I know how much you love me, Thanasis—more than my brother, who has always loved me like it's his duty, and as much as my father, who I never got to know. And I'm grateful. But you know I grew up without my father's love because he went away to America to make a fortune for me to show his love for me, and your love for me is now demanding that I show I'm worthy of it by leaving my husband. Please don't make me do that."

"You don't seem to understand, Panayota. This isn't about me. This is about your life with someone who has already murdered you in his mind over and over again. And he will do it soon if you don't leave him now. He'll find someone with the guts he hasn't got to do it for him."

Panayota sighed. "You know George; he is like a child. He just says what he feels when he feels it. He is so loving when he has forgotten his anger, and now that girl has gone away from the village. Everything will be all right. I know it will be. So let's stop being so gloomy."

"If you're going to continue pretending that nothing's wrong," Thanasis snapped, "I'll talk to that Linatsas myself!"

Panayota felt her heart quiver with fear. "Thanasis," she said, lowering her voice to a whisper, "don't." Unable to remain calm any longer, she could feel her eyes filling up with tears. "I beg of you. Please don't. Can't you see I'm doing everything to save my marriage? If it breaks up, there's nothing left for me to live for."

In all the years she had known him, Panayota had only cried in front of her cousin once—when he had resolved to force George to marry her. As she locked eyes with Thanasis, she could see that he, too, was fighting tears. Chastened, he turned and walked away.

CHAPTER 10:
NO DEAL

MARY PAID A VISIT TO Sakis at his hut, which was located across from Kupaki and halfway up St. Nicholas Hill, and found him alone.

Now an old man, Sakis was a legend whose reputation extended well beyond the rugged village he called home. Barber. Lutist. Clarinet player. Sakis was many things, but most knew him as a brilliant criminal who had committed countless audacious crimes over the years while somehow avoiding arrest. As someone who had outwitted the police and bribed judges, he was most infamous for an incident in the 1930s, when, commissioned by a girl's family to avenge a broken engagement, he carried out the act in the short time it took him to step outside and supposedly answer the call of nature during a concert. While his band continued to play, he disappeared, found his gun, and shot the erstwhile fiancé dead. He returned minutes later, the owner of a built-in alibi.

The fact that Mary had traveled to see someone as lethal as Sakis was a clear indication that the Panaitakis and Mary were running out of wiggle room. Since George Nitsos had returned from his stint with the army in mid-September, he had wasted no time in enlisting the couple in his plot to kill Panayota. He had already sent Mary on several missions to negotiate with potential killers, no doubt certain no one would ever suspect the woman of arranging a murder. Mary and her husband had managed to outmaneuver George by feeding him fictitious information or stretching out negotiations for weeks before feigning disappointment that a deal had fallen through.

When George had suggested she approach Sakis, Mary had felt out of her depth. Now, standing just feet away from the legendary criminal, she felt her throat dry up with fear.

"What is it?" he asked brusquely.

"I'm here on behalf of George Nitsos," Mary said meekly.

Sakis frowned, his eyes forming inscrutable slits. "Linatsas?"

"Yes," Mary answered nervously. "He has a proposal for you."

"Why doesn't he give it to me himself?"

"Oh, well," Mary stammered, "he's very busy."

"Linatsas?" Sakis looked skeptical. "What does the busy man want?"

"Well..." Mary couldn't bring herself to meet the old man's gaze, much less answer his question. "He's offering to pay you to ... kill his wife."

Sakis's eyes flashed something wild and white-hot. Surprise? Anger? Excitement? Mary wasn't sure. He was a cagey old one, impossible to read. He needed less than a second to recover himself and resume his steely countenance.

"How much?" he asked flatly.

Mary swallowed hard. She remembered her husband's words before her departure this morning: *Make it an offer that's easy to refuse.*

"Well," she said tentatively, "Mr. Nitsos has told me to tell you that the fee is negotiable. He—"

"Bah!" Sakis said, cutting her off with a wave of the hand. "Linatsas can do nothing for me." He turned his head slightly, eyeing Mary suspiciously. "And I want nothing from him. You tell him no deal." His eyes, icy until now, twinkled faintly. "Besides, in case you haven't noticed, I'm retired. I gave all that up a long time ago."

Mary felt her shoulders sag with relief. "Of course," she said in a voice barely above a whisper, the words catching in her throat. "I will tell him. Thank you. Good day."

After Sakis refused the job, Mary told George that too many people knew about his plan, and it was time to stop before someone told the authorities. Had George pressed on that fall despite Mary's advice, he might have succeeded, given the civil war now raging all around our village.

PART II

CHAPTER 11:
GUARDIAN ANGEL

FRIEND AGAINST FRIEND. BROTHER AGAINST brother. The civil war divided our region, as it did all of Greece. And thus human life came to matter less than a flower by the side of the road, at the mercy of any boy with a stick. Anyone caught in the wrong place at the wrong time might become the war's next victim.

George, with his con man's instincts, sensed that he couldn't run with the hare and hunt with the hounds forever. He and Panayota moved to Athens and thus removed himself from the daily tit-for-tat of the ongoing war. Living in the relative security of the capital was far safer than risking his life in our remote village. He returned only months later when the Nationalists, courtesy of the Marshall Plan, had gained the upper hand against the Communist guerillas. In fact, he was appointed as commander of his village militia, the aim of which was to assist the local police and tactical military Nationalists' units in their war against the guerillas.

Thirty men in the village, including Thanasis, were conscripted into George's band and were armed with Mannlicher rifles, by then already relics from another era, plus hand grenades, land mines, and a machine gun mounted on a tripod.

Late that summer, Thanasis found himself manning a lonely outpost on the hill of Pyrgos, towering up and to the west of the village.

"Do you see anything?" Panaitakis asked.

"Nothing," Thanasis replied.

The two men had been assigned to monitor the hill while the rest of their unit took up a hidden position on the other side. George had left them with orders to stay put unless they heard otherwise. If a large unit of guerillas was approaching, they would be notified by him and should then beat a hasty retreat at the first opportunity. Such was their mission: they were the eyes and ears of the Nationalist army's regulars, who were close by and better equipped to engage in heavy fighting.

The assignment was nothing unusual. George often split his band into two groups, with one small unit serving as sentinel on one of the surrounding hilltops while the larger unit patrolled or set up an ambush nearby. In this case, all was quiet. There was nothing to do for the two men but talk.

"Did you hear about Linatsas's latest scheme?" Panaitakis groused.

"Which one?" Thanasis asked lazily.

"Last week he found a young girl from the village—beautiful and buxom—and asked her to dress up in a military uniform," Panaitakis said. "She even wore an insignia on her uniform. He escorted her from home to home in the village, introducing her as an army agent whose duty was to collect food supplies for the soldiers fighting up in the mountains. He collected all sorts of cheese, fruit, walnuts, chestnuts, and sweets from the poor villagers, who gladly gave up that night's supper to support the war effort. Then he and his mates threw a party and ate all the food."

Thanasis shook his head in disgust.

"They laughed all night as they recounted the reactions of the villagers as they stole their food," Panaitakis concluded.

"Well, the other day," Thanasis said, taking over, "he was feeling bored and asked the men to use the chimney pots on the rooftops for target practice."

Now it was Panaitakis who was shaking his head.

Shots rang out abruptly on the other side of the hillside, and soon the hills echoed with the sounds of heavy fighting. Thanasis exchanged a knowing glance with Panaitakis. George and the others were engaging the Communists.

"Listen to the small one," Panaitakis said, cocking his head to one side.

Thanasis knew Panaitakis was referring to Socrates Karaiskos, a swarthy man in his mid-twenties. "The small one" had been orphaned at an early age and as a result had spent most of his life in the fields, the exposure to hard work and the elements making him strong. He was well known for his sharpshooting skills and icy disposition. As George's protégé, he had been assigned the operation of the unit's only machine gun.

At the moment, Thanasis and Panaitakis could hear him unleashing several long bursts from his gun on the other side of the hill. The report from the machine gun was deeper and sounded more menacing than the small arms fire intermingled with it.

After a few minutes, the shooting stopped suddenly and was followed by utter silence.

The longer it remained quiet, the more anxious and uncertain Thanasis felt. What was happening? He eyed the horizon guardedly.

"I don't like this," he muttered. "Do you think the big one will forget to notify us if they retreat?"

If Socrates was "the small one," George was "the big one." While Socrates was handy with a gun, George wasn't nearly as adept as the unit's leader.

"From him everything is possible," Panaitakis said. "And that is why someone else should be calling the shots."

"Do you think he's still trying to find someone to kill Panayota?" Thanasis asked, changing the subject.

"From him everything is possible," Panaitakis repeated. "Don't you see how many brainless youth are in his unit? They worship him. Do you think he won't try?"

"I'm afraid you're right."

"I know I'm right," Panaitakis replied. "I—"

Thanasis held up his hand abruptly, signaling Panaitakis to be quiet. Something down the ridgeline had caught his attention.

Panaitakis saw it, too, his eyes narrowing.

An enemy soldier's head bobbed above the scrub grass only about thirty yards away. Then another. Soon several dozen guerillas could be seen working their way up the hillside.

"Linatsas said he would send word!" Panaitakis whispered angrily.

"He lied, as usual." Thanasis slung his gun over his shoulder. "Let's go."

The two men turned to run but were quickly spotted. How they escaped the hail of gunfire from automatic rifles that followed would mystify Thanasis for years to come.

"God, for the sake of our children," he would say later, "had a guardian angel protecting us that day."

———— ✥ ————

Not long afterward, and while the Communist guerillas were being pushed further away from the village, George and Panayota were hosting an evening dinner party at their home. Panayota, having scurried about all day to make sure the home was impeccably tidied and decorated, was now busily looking after their guests. She didn't mind replenishing wine glasses, taking away dirtied dishes, or dressing the part of a beautiful hostess. In fact, she enjoyed entertaining guests and took pride in the reputation she had worked hard to gain as a first-rate cook and homemaker.

If anything nagged at her at all, it was the thought that George might do or say something to put everyone on edge. At the moment, he was standing in the living room with their guests and proudly showing off a gramophone he had recently bought. The story behind its purchase was one he loved to tell again and again.

"My love," he said, interrupting his tale long enough to address his wife, "bring us the wine from the table, would you?"

Panayota blushed. Most people in the village didn't believe in hanging their love for their spouses like banners for all to see. Such terms of endearment between married couples were reserved for private moments. Panayota knew, however, that while most of their dinner party guests would be embarrassed or shocked by the remark, others would find George's boldness charming. It was quite possible one or more of the ladies on hand would feel envious of such lavish talk.

She returned with a bottle of red wine, now half empty, and began topping off their guests' glasses.

"Thank you, darling," George said, eying her sweetly.

Again, her face flushed red.

The past several months had been a whirlwind, full of upheaval and conflict. Between the war and their many moves, she oftentimes had felt literally out of breath. It felt good to be back in her village, amongst friends and family. True, many of the people they entertained were military officers and their wives, just passing through, or government officials, also on their way to somewhere else.

"Bring me an ashtray," George said.

Panayota, who was talking to an officer's wife, didn't hear him until too late.

"Bring the ashtray, and fuck your Christ!"

The room, bubbling with conversation just a second earlier, fell deathly silent.

Panayota felt the blood drain from her cheeks. She hurried to the kitchen and returned with an ashtray, smiling the whole time, hoping the others would see that her husband was just joking.

But George wasn't finished. "You whore," he spat, turning over the bottle of wine he had just drained. "Not even a fucking drop of wine in the bottle. How many times have I told you to take away bottles as soon as they're empty and put a full bottle on the table?"

"But we're not at the table," Panayota protested. "We're—"

"Just bring us more wine!" George snapped.

Panayota did as she was told, all the while wishing she could disappear. George was on a tear that night, and soon he was repeating the old joke about giving his wife away with a dowry if there were any takers. To her shame, all Panayota could do was joke along.

Thanasis wasn't sorry when one day the news circulated amongst the villagers that the commander had been shot by the Communists and probably killed during an encounter on the village outskirts. Unfortunately, the wounded hero arrived a little later that day with nothing more than a scratch on his upper arm.

"The vicious old dog will be the last to die after eating all of his master's animals," Thanasis said to Panaitakis, repeating an old proverb. "And now the bastard will get promoted, won't he?"

Panaitakis nodded in agreement.

A few weeks later, George was promoted to second lieutenant.

CHAPTER 12:
BUSINESS PARTNERS
AND OPPOSITES

BY THE BEGINNING OF 1949, most of the Communist guerillas had been defeated, captured, or driven away, and all of the villagers who had abandoned Kupaki for a safer environment had finally returned home.

On Easter Sunday that spring, I remember gathering with my brothers behind George's right-hand man, Socrates Karaiskos, shortly after Easter services and watching in awe as the sharpshooter set up his Gladiator machine gun on its tripod in the middle of the churchyard. The church bells were still ringing in celebration of the holy resurrection when George gave the order to fire. Socrates responded by unleashing a hail of bullets that ricocheted off the huge boulders across the ravine near the cemetery of St. Anthony.

As I watched smoke rise from the battered rocks in the distance, I felt nothing but admiration for George Nitsos and Socrates Karaiskos. These were potent men unafraid to wield their authority in a garish display of raw power.

Although some in the village, including Thanasis, thought George Nitsos was a bully who misused his authority, there were those of us who were impressed by his raw displays of power. None of the adults in our village seemed interested in challenging him. He had money. He had prestige. He had connections. If a government agent, policeman, military officer—anyone in a uniform—visited our village, he invariably went to George Nitsos first.

As a sense of normalcy returned to the village, new problems arose, problems that had nothing to do with fighting and everything to do with day-to-day living.

The village's store owner had decided to sell his store, and Thanasis had spoken to him offering to take over the store himself. George was also making noises about reopening a store next door that years earlier had belonged to his uncle. A footpath no wider than four feet separated the two building's front yards.

"Cousin," Panayota said one day after approaching Thanasis, "would you consider becoming business partners with my husband?"

Thanasis offered a look of disbelief. He didn't know whether to be incredulous, indignant, or both.

"Hear me out," Panayota said. "I know you have had your share of misgivings about George, but wouldn't it be better to have one large business together than two smaller businesses that must compete with each other? Why not become partners?"

Thanasis couldn't deny the logic in his cousin's argument. But going into business with a scoundrel like Linatsas struck him as foolhardy at best. George was irresponsible. Untrustworthy. Lazy. Would his reputation, not to mention the lamb-stealing story behind his nickname, undermine potential customers' trust? He would probably leave all the work to Thanasis, all the while provoking him into one needless argument after another.

No, Thanasis thought, the two men were far too different, and the list of reasons not to go into business with Linatsas was far too long. He opened his mouth to say no but hesitated when he saw the look on Panayota's face.

"You'll be less likely to argue if you're partners, rather than competitors," she said. "And I don't like it when you and George fight."

Her eyes, pleading and vulnerable, told Thanasis this had nothing to do with business. This was a cry for help. It was likely his cousin had convinced herself that she was merely suggesting a prudent consolidation of effort and resources, but in reality she was asking for protection. With the war over, George had nothing to distract him from what had been his prewar obsession: the murder of his wife. Panayota, Thanasis suddenly realized, wanted to keep him close to the man who might kill her one day, to the husband she could never bring herself to leave.

Thanasis smiled gently at his cousin. She had always loved him like a brother, respected him like a father, and joked with and scolded him like a child. She trusted him instinctually—the same way she was now trying to pull him closer. It was doubtful she had thought too deeply about her reasons for suggesting he form a business partnership with her husband. But he nevertheless felt compelled to honor her proposition. He thought back to his courtship of Polyxeni, to the days when he had let his loyalty to his family, particularly his father and his insistence on a handsome dowry, interfere with his love for Polyxeni. It was Panayota who had pulled him roughly into the light. Afterward, telling his father that Polyxeni was worth a thousand dowries had been the easiest thing in the world.

"All right," Thanasis said. "I'll consider it, Cousin."

In fact, as much as Thanasis distrusted George, he couldn't deny that there were good reasons for going into business with the man. George had worked at several large stores in Patras and thus had plenty of retail experience. He was a natural salesman—charming and persuasive. He certainly had the right contacts, not to mention a knack for making deals and striking bargains. And no one was more resourceful.

Suddenly Thanasis's misgivings seemed unimportant. Of course, it was one thing to talk himself into joining forces with George. It would be quite another to convince Polyxeni, his wife, that going into business with George Nitsos was a sound idea. Polyxeni knew nothing of the dangers Panayota was facing, and Thanasis, intent on protecting her and us children, wanted to keep it that way.

When he presented the idea to Polyxeni, she offered a simple reply.

"As long as you remain only his business partner and do not become like him I can see nothing wrong with it. And as long as you come home the same husband I have known and the same father our children have known, all should be fine."

The store had only been open a few months before its owners clashed. The trouble began when a fresh round of American aid poured into our village, which, like the rest of Greece, was still benefiting from the Marshall Plan. George, the most connected man in Kupaki, was entrusted by government officials to oversee distribution, which would be based on the size and needs of each family. Some of the supplies were initially stocked at the old store George's uncle had owned, and some found their way to the store being run by George and Thanasis. It wasn't long before rumors began to spread that George, who had access to both stockpiles, was secretly hording the food and supplies and passing them out to his friends. Some were even saying Thanasis was involved.

That was when, a disgruntled older villager who had received nothing in the way of food or supplies, showed up at the store with a frown on his face.

"George Nitsos," said the villager, addressing George, who was standing behind the counter, "I want to know where my share of the aid is. Did you give it to your friends? Or do you still have it hidden away back there?"

He nodded to the back room.

George didn't bother with a reply. Instead, he slapped the other man across the face. The incident upset Thanasis gravely and made him wonder if he and his partner had anything at all in common. Their friendship, if anyone dared call it that, was polite but reserved. Although they walked the same steep paths and drank from the same village spring every day, they were worlds apart. Thanasis was a loyal husband, a family man, the proud father of four children. He respected his fellow villagers and believed in simple virtues like honesty and hard work.

George, on the other hand, remained a mystery. Though approaching forty, he ran with a younger crowd, bachelors mostly, who often behaved more like cronies than friends.Many of his youthful friends were fleeing to the cities, where opportunities were multiplying in the wake of American aid. Thus, George's circle of friends had recently begun to dwindle.

In the days that followed, more resentful villagers, who were aware of the amount of provisions present in the houses of George's friends, brought their complaints to George, and each time he turned on them.

Thanasis then realized he'd made a grave mistake in opening a store with him. When he confronted George over the matter, an argument ensued, and a few days later George had transferred his share to his uncle's old store. Now the villagers were forced to choose between the two stores when shopping for supplies. Predictably, they split almost exclusively along family lines.

Panayota, though, refused to allow the division to remain. For three months, she went back and forth between the two men, trotting out the same arguments she had used on Thanasis before the partnership had begun. Once again, Thanasis gave in, and George moved his merchandise back to Thanasis's store. Thanasis and George were partners again.

As the partnership resumed, Thanasis managed the store's butcher shop while George managed the groceries—a proposal Panayota had made in order to keep the two men together yet separate under the same roof. Thanasis soon realized he was doing most of the work, but he didn't make an issue of it.

George, always more interested in partying and socializing than in working, also spent many days hunting. His most exclusive hunting partner and closest friend and protégé was Socrates Karaiskos. "The small one," as he had been known during the civil war, was in his mid-twenties. Taciturn, unemotional, cold, he was the opposite of his flamboyant ex-commander. Extraordinarily robust, he was George's strong arm. Thanasis often wondered if he was even human, or merely a machine. When he hunted for rabbits with George and the others, he was reputed to rarely miss his mark. After firing the lethal bullet, he would stand aloof and expressionless, his still-smoking gun in his hands, while the dogs sniffed wildly at the rabbit's still warm corpse.

As manager of the groceries and their inventory, George, instead of travelling to nearby towns, often proposed to go to Athens on the pretext of finding better prices.

True, the capital's bustling market offered more competition and lower prices, but Athens also happened to be where many of George's relatives lived. He could visit and stay with them and of course see his young friends who had recently moved there.

What Thanasis didn't know—and what would only come to light years later—was that after shopping at the market and spending time with his relations, George would then avail himself of what he had really traveled to Athens for: the wild life. Most of George's trips to Athens led to a night on the town. He would meet a handful of his old cronies, now policemen in Athens, at Omonoia Square downtown Athens and invite them to dinner at an expensive restaurant nearby, offering to pay for all those who seemed hesitant to go because of the cost. After several hours of feasting, drinking, and dancing at the restaurant, he would ask them to show him around their fair city. They would oblige, cringing in embarrassment as they carried the lurching and loudmouthed man, now unable to walk on his own powers.

Next, he would cajole them into taking him for a stroll through the red light district. Some would assume it was curiosity leading him on. But those who had joined him in the past for one of his nights of debauchery would know better. Embarrassed to be seen amongst prostitutes and pimps, his uninitiated policemen friends would assume he merely wanted to ogle the women standing in the open doorways. After all, someone married to the likes of Panayota would never squander his time by spending it with prostitutes. But George would disappear inside, leaving his friends to pace outside while he finished his business. Then he would emerge, composing lurid, graphic verses about his just-completed conquest and singing them loudly in the street.

CHAPTER 13:
BEST FRIENDS

AFTER TUCKING US INTO BED one night, Polyxeni said goodnight to my siblings and me and then left for my parents' bedroom, where an oil lamp hanging from a wall peg cast a warm glow. Thanasis, as seemed to happen whenever George was out of town, was late. And Mother had a hunch she knew who he was with: Panayota.

Polyxeni slipped under the covers and then, after propping her head up on her elbow, reached with her free hand toward the lamp to lower the wick. A second later, the room was only dimly lit, with long shadows arcing across the floor.

Thanasis, she wondered, *what are you up to?*

As she stared up at the ceiling, her eyes slowly adjusting to the faded light, she tried to suppress the suspicion welling inside her. She knew well that one of the reasons she and Thanasis were husband and wife was because his cousin had lobbied so hard for him to her—and for her to him. And Panayota had been right: he had turned out to be a fine husband and father. Where was he now? Why had he missed supper?

When she heard the faint sound of the front door creaking open, she knew she would have an answer shortly. A moment later, Thanasis was lowering his body to the bed and emitting a tired sigh.

She rolled over to face him. "Where have you been?"

"I was at the Nitsos house—talking to Panayota."

Polyxeni briefly considered letting it go at that but then thought better of it. "What is this, Thanasis? It seems you visit your cousin every evening when her husband is not home."

"I needed to talk to her."

"Always when George leaves? Is it something he cannot hear?"

Would he think she was jealous? Would he respond with evasiveness? She hadn't thought much about how he might react to her interrogation, but no amount of pondering could have prepared her for his reply.

"Listen, Polyxeni. George Nitsos has been trying to find someone to kill Panayota."

She gasped in disbelief. "What?"

"George has been planning this for years. He's actively looking for someone to do the deed."

Polyxeni still couldn't believe her ears. "Well, well," she said. "Is he going to slaughter her like a lamb? Who did Nitsos approach to do his dirty work for him?"

"A better question would be who he *hasn't* approached. He tried to hire Panaitakis and Mary several years ago, and this month two more people came to me with stories of him trying to hire them to murder Panayota. He is promising them money or other rewards if they do it."

"But surely, Thanasis," she said, interrupting his list, "George Nitsos can't be that dumb. I can believe he's Godless enough to do that, but I never thought he was that stupid."

"But he's not stupid," Thanasis countered. "He's counting on people like you and me to assume he could never be so foolish as to ask an old woman like Mary or whoever else to murder his wife. That's all part of his plan. This is his clever mind at work. If anyone tries to confront him, he can easily deny the whole thing. Can't you see him now denying it? The fact that so many people are in on it can work in his favor. He can say the same thing as you, that it would be utterly foolish to plan such a thing and tell so many people. Who would believe such a thing?"

Polyxeni thought for a moment. She was still skeptical, but she could tell by the solemn look on Thanasis's face that he was worried. "And you say two more people approached you this month to tell you this?"

"Yes. That's why I went to see Panayota tonight after closing the store. I told her she must leave him, but she won't. She can't bear the thought of being the only divorced woman in Kupaki."

"These are just his empty threats to scare Panayota," Polyxeni said. She was determined to put Thanasis's mind at rest. "And empty threats they will remain. George Nitsos is like the air outside. Sometimes cool, sometimes hot. Sometimes strong, sometimes weak. Sometimes easterly, sometimes westerly. But never stable."

Having been reassured by his wife that George Nitsos was all talk, Thanasis began to concentrate more on his work and his family. He even joined George in another business venture, investing jointly in livestock the Panaitakis and Mary were looking after. Although teaming up with George made Thanasis queasy, he couldn't deny the social benefits. After all, George was one of the most important men in the village, what with his military rank, his part ownership of the store, and his marriage to Panayota, beloved by all. And of course there was the money that kept arriving in envelopes from America, courtesy of George's father.

George, unfortunately, was all too aware of his influence in the village and grew increasingly arrogant as a result. He was especially intolerable toward women. He was good at earning money for the store—when he deigned to work, which occurred in spurts but just often enough for Thanasis to turn a blind eye to his excesses.

"George knows how to sell," Thanasis would say. The man used all the means at his disposal, including his contacts with influential people. If nothing else, Thanasis thought, keeping George close allowed him to continue to watch over and protect Panayota.

When George was elected village president, his ego grew even more bloated. "Because I am Nitsos," was the answer he gave many hapless people who dared question his judgment in municipal matters.

His arrogance extended to his horsemanship and to his horse Kitsos, an excitable and unpredictable animal. Several young, athletic men, including Socrates Karaiskos, the strongest man in the village at the time and George's closest friend, had been unable to tame the animal. Soon after George took it for a brief successful ride, the horse broke into a gallop while he was on it, jumping and kicking for no apparent reason. George held on for a moment before he was thrown. He broke his leg in the fall and was forced to leave the village for a time to convalesce, only to return a few weeks later on a log stretcher.

Like many of the other children in the village, I was crestfallen after George's accident and throughout his absence. We children had hoped to witness the second coming of Alexander the Great, the great ruler who had once tamed the legendary wild horse, Bucephalus. But we had warm feelings toward George for other reasons, as well. He had just replaced Vasilios, whose authority as a village warden we hated, with his best friend Socrates Karaiskos.

Socrates, "the small guy" of the civil war, had recently bought a house near the center of the village and had married and started a family. At his wedding, he had chosen George, his mentor, as his best man. It was never explained how George had managed to give the village warden job to Socrates, who was barely literate, or how he had taken it away from Vasilios, a long-time adversary. Such appointments required a certain amount of paperwork and had to be approved by a dense bureaucracy. Was this a small coup?

All that anyone knew was that Socrates had ingratiated himself to George, enough to warrant a huge favor, and was by all accounts a member of the family. Even Panayota, the godmother of his baby girl, looked after him, showering him and his young wife with advice, money, and gifts.

Vasilios, meanwhile, had no choice but to accept his role as the odd man out. His relationship with George would only continue to fray.

In every village in Greece, lunch was always followed by a strictly observed siesta, especially in the hot summer, when the stifling afternoon heat was best avoided. In Kupaki, villagers would while away the time indoors, out of reach of the hot sun.

One day Kostas, my older brother, didn't feel like resting. While the rest of the village napped, he and one of his friends loitered near the store, which was presently locked up and deserted.

Kostas, bored, kicked at a small stone. "There's nothing to do," he said forlornly. He didn't like how lonely the store felt. Normally, men smoked out front, or played cards, or absentmindedly fingered their worry beads, but right now those same men were wasting their lives in bed.

His friend, as if reading his mind, pointed to several packs of cigarettes that were staring at them from inside the store. "We could smoke like the men," he offered.

Kostas peered through the small window and noticed decks of cards not far from the cigarettes. "And we could play cards," he added.

The only thing preventing them from carrying on in place of the men was a set of iron bars covering the window.

Kostas tried to reach through the bars, but his arm wasn't nearly long enough.

"Here," his friend said and handed him a stick.

My brother extended the stick past the iron bars and through the open window but, try as he might, still couldn't reach the cards.

He was just about to give up when an idea hit him. "I'll get the key!" he said excitedly.

Kostas raced home and a moment later returned with the key to the front door. He then unlocked the door, and the two eight-year-old boys snuck inside and snatched a pack of cigarettes and some playing cards. With their loot securely in hand, they bolted out the same way they had come, giggling and throwing furtive glances over their shoulders as they raced to their favorite hiding place.

My brother knew he had violated our father's trust, but at the same time, he couldn't deny how exciting it felt to be doing something so disobedient. Like his friend, he was panting hard by the time they reached his friend's family-owned fields, which sat adjacent to the church. There they plunked down beneath a shade tree and opened their pack of cigarettes and deck of cards, and soon they were giddy from the nicotine high.

Before they could come down on their own, they were spooked by the sight of Socrates Karaiskos's dark face peering down at them. Socrates, who lived near the store, had seen everything.

The comeuppance that followed wasn't pretty. As soon as our mother learned of Kostas's treachery, she beat him. His friend collected the same treatment from his mother. Word then came from George that someone had stolen four hundred drachmas from the store's cash register. Another round of beatings followed. By the time Thanasis returned from the fields, Kostas and his friend had each been interrogated, but each boy was maintaining his innocence where the stolen money was concerned.

His friend's uncle, Basil, meanwhile, spoke with Thanasis about the matter. An attorney and notary public, Basil was by nature a gentle and sophisticated man, a fatherly figure who looked after his orphaned nephew. He suggested the adults wait a day or two for the boys to succumb to the guilt that surely must be plaguing them, if indeed they had stolen the money. Thanasis agreed. Neither boy ever confessed to the crime. The truth, though, eventually came out when someone from the village came forward and admitted that George had given the store money that day to one of his cronies in the village, one of the young men that helped constitute his gang.

Basil had been right. A guilty conscience had eventually produced the truth, but that conscience hadn't belonged to my brother or his friend.

CHAPTER 14:
HEART IN THE RIGHT PLACE

IN 1952, THE CELEBRATION ON Shrove Sunday, the Sunday before Lent, degenerated into surreal debauchery when George Nitsos and several of his toadies descended on the village square. It all began shortly after lunch on a sunny spring afternoon. George and his gang assembled in an abandoned barn on Kupaki's southwestern fringe and began to try on various costumes and masks.

Dressed in two pairs of pants, one for its hind legs and the other for its forelegs, Socrates Karaiskos's donkey stood at the center of the mayhem. As the poor animal staggered along, several costumed men were taking turns riding it, although none lasted long before sliding off its back.

George led this motley group into the front yard of his next-door neighbor, and from there, with the help of the donkey's master, they advanced to the central square, where all the villagers had assembled in reaction to all the commotion. As the group started line-dancing, the donkey, thoroughly spooked by now, suddenly emptied its bowels while simultaneously braying in alarm and was thus able to escape its tormentors, most of whom scattered, their hands covering their noses.

Just then, a diminutive female figure appeared. She was dressed in full police regalia. When it became clear she was scaring some of the young children, she removed her police cap, shook her hair free, and offered a reassuring smile. It was Panayota. Several villagers breathed a sigh of relief. Wasn't that just like her? Everyone who knew Panayota was caring and sensitive and would never wish to frighten anyone, especially children.

Those of us watching had hardly exhaled when Panayota began to rip at her uniform and pull at her hair, digging her nails into her flesh and rocking back and forth. Was she possessed? Drunk? Only later would we learn that she had been driven to hysteria by George, who had argued with her violently that day, most likely even beating her, before leaving for his merrymaking.

Panayota, not normally so erratic, was by nature a gentle soul. It was obvious by the way she treated us Konandreas kids—showering us with hugs, kisses, and encouragement whenever she saw us—that she desperately wanted children of her own. Never mind the fact that George Nitsos behaved like a spoilt child himself, demanding all of her attention while insulting her and treating her uncaringly. She even looked into adoption at one point, although unsuccessfully.

While Panayota acted like a tender mother toward the children of the village, George preferred the role of older brother. He clearly wanted to be our hero and was willing to do anything, including teaching us the facts of life long before we were ready to hear them, to win our adulation.

His behavior was at its worst when he was in the company of adolescent girls.

"You were born to make me suffer," he would call out to them as they passed the store, staring at their budding breasts.

Some of the men in the village, including Vasilios, the man whose job as village warden George had given to Socrates, warned him sternly to steer clear of their womenfolk. As the father of two pretty daughters in their late teens, Vasilios knew they were often the object of George's amorous advances.

When George crossed the line at a baptism in September of that year, it was Panayota who stepped in to save him.

Vasilios, having learned that George had positioned himself during the post-ceremony dance so that he could grab the girls' skirts as they passed by his chair, stormed through George's front door later that day.

"I could kill you today!" he shouted. He then nodded to Panayota. "But I don't want to make this good woman a widow. But try your tricks with my girls again and I'll blow the brains clean out of that dirty head of yours!"

"Come on," George said, "it was just a joke."

George's reply only further enraged Vasilios, whose beet-red face looked ready to burst.

Panayota stepped in and managed to calm the indignant father with her soft words and charm. "My husband meant no harm," she said in a soothing voice. "He sometimes pushes too hard for a laugh, but his heart is in the right place."

Fortunately for George, most people in the village seemed to agree with Panayota's assessment. Good old George sometimes did or said things that were risqué, but he was harmless.

My parents were among the few who saw him for what he was.

"If I was your wife," Polyxeni once told him after hearing him hurl the usual vulgar abuse at Panayota, "we wouldn't have lasted an hour."

One night while my parents were cleaning up in the kitchen after dinner, my siblings and I were in our bedroom and doing everything we could to delay going to bed. We decided to play shop.

"Lesini is the watermelon!" Kostas announced, echoing George's famous sales cry. "Argos is the melon!"

"Herrings and sardines!" I retorted, not to be outdone.

We were talking loud enough for Thanasis to hear us, and I'm sure he was reacting to our playacting with some pride, although it's doubtful he appreciated the adoration in our voices as we mimicked his business partner.

But that pride certainly must have disappeared after Panos joined us in the concluding chorus. "Buy, fuck your Holy Virgin!"

Father rushed into our room, with Mother hot on his heels.

"What kind of language is this?" he demanded angrily.

My brothers and I cowered in the furthest corner of the bed, a heavy blanket pulled up to our chins. I was certain we were all about to be spanked, but relief followed when our father made it clear he simply wanted to establish *why* we had gotten it into our heads to say such an awful thing.

"Uncle Nitsos says that all the time," Kostas said.

"I know he does," Thanasis replied sternly, "but that doesn't mean you have to repeat it."

"But he's your partner!" I pointed out. "He does that at the store all the time."

"He's my partner, not my son," Thanasis retorted. "It's not my duty to bring him up properly. I know what to take from him and what not to. You don't. I have never repeated the filthy things he says.

You did. So I'm asking you now to stop imitating everything he says and does. And don't you ever repeat what you said."

Although I was confused, I nodded with the others. It didn't seem fair that adults could say things that children weren't allowed to repeat. One thing that *was* beginning to sink in, however, was that not everybody admired George the way we kids did.

CHAPTER 15:
THEN YOU WOULD KNOW

GEORGE NITSOS DIDN'T BOTHER TO hide his lecherous gaze. As the new schoolteacher studied, the damaged by time house of one of his friends, George let his eyes wander the graceful lines of her supple body.

The schoolteacher, young and unmarried, had arrived a few weeks earlier just in time for the new school year. Some said she was too young and had only a few months of teaching experience. Others said she had a way with the children that encouraged them to work harder. All George cared about was that she was easy on the eyes—fresh meat, as it were, for a man whose appetites were not easily satisfied. He had arranged for her to stay at the house across the street from his house.

A few weeks after her arrival, she had been appointed to a local committee whose duties included examining buildings that had been burned down during the German and Italian occupations and the civil war. At the moment, she was viewing what was left of a house that belonged to one of George's friends. Her report would help determine how much, if any, government aid would be granted to help fund renovation.

George felt his patience ebb; he knew his flattery was having little impact on the teacher. Indeed, she had a serious, no-nonsense air about her that grated. She appeared impervious to his charms. Most girls blushed when he flirted with them, but she kept him at arm's length. She had to be aware of her own attractiveness, her fresh good looks, her youthful allure. She positively oozed sensuality. And yet here she was going about her business as if her only intention was to appraise this building. Her aloofness was maddening.

George, impatiently shifting his weight from one foot to the other, glanced away at the surrounding hillsides, which would soon begin to show fall color.

The village vacationers had already completed their mass exodus for the heated apartments and schools of crowded Athens. The swallows, too, had abandoned their mud nests so carefully constructed in balconies all over the village and migrated south, toward the warm shores of North Africa. With flocks flying overhead, Kupaki's shepherds had left the open hilltops around the village and made for the lowlands and their sheep cots and manger-like enclosures. Fall was an exciting time of transition, George thought, a sensual feast of riotous colors and bold scents. But it was lost on this dour schoolteacher.

Finally the schoolteacher was ready to offer her assessment. "I'm sorry this man's house is in such bad condition, Mr. Nitsos," she said. "But I cannot attest that the damage has been caused by fire. I see no evidence of that."

George unfolded one of his patented smiles. "I can assure you this place was burnt down during the occupation," he said, unleashing all his charm. "I've seen many such buildings during my time as commander."

"And I have lived all my life in a village," the fetching young schoolteacher responded. "My house is built with the same materials as this one. I know how burnt wood and stone look, and it's definitely not like this."

George felt his jaw drop. His charisma was obviously wasted on this pathetic excuse for a girl.

"I'll hang up your bread, you bitch!" he shouted, referring to the way villagers hung their loaves from trees to prevent foxes and other scavenging animals from eating them.

Fortunately for our new schoolteacher, George spent most of the winter in nearby towns. As our village's council president, he sat in on several meetings dedicated to the construction of a new road connecting Kupaki with several area villages. In fact, nobody thought much about his frequent absences. Only later would we learn that between these meetings there were a few romantic ones, as well.

He returned in the spring of 1953 in a festive mood and organized several village-wide celebrations, including an extravagant affair for his namesake on St. George's Day. His behavior that day hardly resembled the legendary saint's, as he insulted and slapped Panayota in front of several well-wishers in his house.

On May Day 1953, true to Greek tradition, our village celebrated with a grand picnic atop a small peak that rose just southwest of the village. To usher in the spectacular spring day, the schoolteacher led us schoolchildren to a fitting opening ceremony with a song about flowers and wreaths she had been teaching us for days.

The villagers lined the saddles of their horses with multicolored homespun blankets and loaded the animals with satchels bulging with picnic food and wicker-cradled demijohns filled with *ouzo* and local red wine for the half-hour trek.

After reaching the summit, we took in the glorious view, which encompassed several nearby villages, plus the River Mornos and some of its tributaries. Soon spits were erected by the more energetic of the adults, while others, mostly the older among them, happily spread blankets on the ground nearby and flopped down to rest. Later that afternoon, after the meal, the villagers, aided by red wine, danced the traditional line Greek dances, with Thanasis and Panayota leading the revelry.

While everybody was mixing it up with everybody, dancing and exchanging wishes, George was exclusively in the company of the local police captain. They did not dance but instead murmured to each other whenever a pretty young maiden led the dance. The villagers knew George and the captain were good friends, often visiting each other during the past few months, but it was always thought the ex-captain and the new were just bodies joined by the fate of authority.

By the time the dancing finally came to an end, many of the men were so drunk they were betting on who could roll downhill the farthest. While cheered by everyone, Thanasis, his face flushed, kept singing and dancing but his steps were no longer surefooted. I could see Polyxeni was not pleased with his condition. She had bruised her shin after falling from her horse during the ride to the summit and thus had been watching the dancing instead of participating. She laughed at Father's behavior at first, but now I could tell she was ready to put her foot down.

"Thanasis," she said firmly, "that's enough. You'll get sick. Time to go home."

When some other men's wives also intervened by asking their husbands to stop, the men, including Thanasis, pretended—and declared with much hand-gesturing—that they had no knowledge who the women were and had never met them in their lives. The situation further aggravated Polyxeni.

Panayota stepped in, saying, "Let the men have fun, Polyxeni dear." She was giggling like a schoolgirl. "They're doing fine. It's only a little wine."

Her words, unfortunately, did nothing to appease Polyxeni, who told her as much.

Panayota, giggling a second earlier, stopped abruptly, the mirth in her eyes disappearing like the flame of a snuffed-out candle. "You should have someone else, Polyxeni," she said, her eyes moving to stare at George, "to tell you every day, 'Fuck your virgin and your God.' Then you would know!"

Her words had a humbling effect on Polyxeni, as they did on me.

Father, though, appeared ready to go home. As he staggered off in the vague direction of our village, still mumbling the lyrics to the song, I knew he had just enough presence of mind to find his way home.

CHAPTER 16:
NOBODY TO TALK TO

THE FESTIVALS CONTINUED INTO SUMMER, and beginning July 25, the village celebrated a two-day fair. Everyone gathered in the village square to eat, socialize, and dance.

Central square dancing. Alekos Tsipras, the teacher of philosophy, is holding Tina Taratsas, who leads. At the top of the photo, spectators have gathered in the front yard of the store belonging to George and Thanasis. The bottom of the photo is near the spot where Panayota read George's love letter to Poly.

As usual, George and Thanasis had a bird's-eye view of the celebration from their store, which overlooked the square. But when the dancing started at 6:30 pm that evening, it would have been better had George not been able to see Poly, his erstwhile love interest, who had returned from Athens to partake in the festivities. Now in her mid-twenties, Poly was a striking beauty, and she made a lovely dancing partner for Georges Gumas, her cousin and my uncle, a handsome air force man with startling blue eyes and an athletic build. Dressed in his immaculately clean and pressed white uniform, he took hold of Poly's kerchief and joined her as they led the circular Greek dance at the exact spot where Panayota had stood and read aloud the letter sent by George to her some years ago.

All eyes seemed to follow the couple putting on a brilliant display of grace and beauty. Furtively, one by one, the villagers began to shift their gaze from the attractive couple to the man who had once besieged her and had scandalously vied for her affections until her father had been forced to take her away. They wanted to see how George would react to the sight of Poly's lips, which were parted like a half-opened rose, as she smiled to her cousin, now holding her. How would her former illicit suitor respond as she spun gracefully in another man's hands just a few yards away?

The display appeared to set George on fire. He took a drag from his cigarette, inhaling deeply, and then jerked his gaze away from the dashing couple and stared down at the slate tiles beneath his feet.

After that night, George rarely played cards at the store. His jokes grew less profane, and he could be seen spending more time in lonely contemplation on a bench at the store.

Panayota, meanwhile, seemed happier than she had been for some time.

"Our prayers are answered," Polyxeni told Thanasis one night. "Thanks to the Holy Virgin, there is peace again under Panayota's and George's roof. Long may it last."

Panayota was always so cheerful and ladylike; hearing George utter blasphemous vulgarities against her had shocked Polyxeni to the core. Polyxeni had no idea what it was like to be mistreated by a husband, to live in a world of abuse and fear.

Now, though, it appeared things were finally improving between the couple, but Polyxeni's euphoria didn't last long.

Just days later, her sister-in-law Papadia, Papazois's wife, relayed to her an early-morning encounter she'd had with Panayota.

"I found Panayota sleeping in a barn just on the outskirts of the village," Papadia told Polyxeni. "She tried to deny it at first, but then she cried and admitted things aren't going well with George. I told her she should divorce the man, but she refuses. She doesn't want to be the subject of village gossip. She doesn't want to be Panayota Soulias again."

The fact that Panayota was spending nights sleeping outside her house made Polyxeni agonize over her safety. Had Thanasis been wise to take George's machinations seriously?

Toward the end of August 1953, Panayota was watering the beans in her garden near the spring of Motsu, when Marula, whose house butted up against the garden, approached her.

"How is the crop, Panayota?" Marula asked as she entered the garden.

"Hello, Marula. The crop is fine."

Marula, like Panayota, was a slender woman who stood less than five feet tall. The bean plants, supported by cedar stakes, towered over her, forming a maze of arches overhead. The sound of trickling water could be heard from the nearest ditch, not to mention the irrigation pool nearby, although it was nearly drowned out by the buzzing of bees pollinating the bean flowers overhead.

"Panayota," Marula said in a soft voice, "I have something I need to tell you."

Panayota straightened. "What is it?"

"Effie saw your husband kissing Katina outside the store and then again inside. She was so shocked to see a married man kissing a young woman that she didn't know what to do. She is a very ethical girl and finally came to me at the village spring and confessed what she saw. She asked me not to tell anyone because she is afraid of George, but I knew I must tell you. You have a right to know."

Panayota felt the blood drain from her face. Effie was Marula's goddaughter. She was young, but trustworthy. If she said it was true, then it was likely true. As for Katina, she was a pretty young brunette who carried herself with a poise that made her look older than what she really was: eighteen. What had George gone and done? Panayota wanted to deny the story, to say there must be some kind of mistake. But she knew there was no point.

"Did anyone else see this?" she finally asked.

"No. Only my Effie."

"And she has told no one else?"

"No one."

Her secret, Panayota knew, wouldn't stay that way for long, not in Kupaki. "Oh, dear Marula!" she lamented. "I have great, great many troubles, and I have nobody to talk to!"

"You have nobody to talk to?" Marula countered. "You have cousins and cousins here, and you have a brother and sister you can write, and you tell me you have nobody to talk to? Go and talk to them, you. Go and talk to them. What are you waiting for?"

Panayota did have several blood relations in the village, but she spoke to only one person about George's secret: Effie. She met her on a village path one day and told her that the gossip she was spreading about her husband was damaging his reputation in the village. Effie, clearly embarrassed, pretended she knew nothing and had spoken to nobody. It was obvious she was afraid of George.

See Dramatis Personae at the end of the book.

PART III

CHAPTER 17:
CRACKS IN THE FAÇADE

ON SUNDAY, SEPTEMBER 6, 1953, I watched from the altar of St. George Church as my fellow villagers, responding to the invitation of the bells pealing overhead, began to arrive for the morning service. The spiritual hub of our small village, St. George was so old that no one, not even the oldest men with ancient shepherds' crooks in their gnarled old hands, had seen the raising of its walls, now cracked.

Kupaki's St. George Church in 1951. The walls, still cracked, had yet to undergo renovation. Papazois, the priest, stands at the entrance.

At eight years old, I had been made an altar boy by Papazois, the village priest. Papazois, wore a gold-colored robe and a long, flowing white beard. The smell of stone, wood, and incense filled me with a sense of contentment, as did the sight of everyone dressed in their Sunday best. As the villagers entered, their shoes making muffled sounds on the stone, they brought with them wafts of newly laundered clothes and fresh tobacco. I counted them idly, eventually topping out at about one hundred and twenty people, half of which were visitors who would be leaving when the weather turned cold.

The men, taking their customary place, assembled to the right of the center aisle, while the women gathered to the left. Several church council members sat behind the counter near the back of the nave, including Thanasis, who was the vice president, and George Nitsos, the president.

"With fear of God," Papazois proclaimed, his voice softened by his long white beard, "faith and love, draw near."

As he chanted, he lifted with both hands the holy chalice, which was covered with a scarlet veil.

Most parishioners moved forward to receive Communion, but George left the counter, took a couple steps toward Papazois, and then, as if remembering something, changed course toward the doors.

"Receive me today, oh Son of God," Papazois said, "as a partaker of the Mystic Feast."

One by one the pious made the sign of the cross and approached the priest. With the scarlet veil under their chins, they opened their mouths to receive the bread and the wine, the flesh and the blood of the Savior.

"For the deliverance of sins and for eternal life..."

Once outside, George walked across the churchyard toward a huge mulberry tree beside the compound's low stone wall. Shaded from the sun by the tree's enormous canopy, he sat down on the wall and faced the church. From the thick shade he studied the spectacular panorama of rolling hills and mountain peaks that opened up in every direction. He fumbled in his pockets and, after fishing a cigarette free, lit it and drew the smoke into his lungs hungrily.

He didn't notice Katina, who had exited her house next to the church compound, until she was walking confidently toward him.

"Just came to say hello," the pretty young brunette said after he gave her a questioning look.

"Hello."

"Do you want me to bring you a chair?" she asked.

George didn't answer, and instead waved her away. As she left, he trained his gaze on the church.

At the end of the service, Papazois stood benignly at the altar and addressed the parishioners. "May the Holy Trinity watch over you. Good morning."

"*Kalimera, Papuli,*" each parishioner replied while approaching him again to accept a piece of the Holy Bread from the hand of the priest. "Good morning, Grandfather."

Soon little groups of people started to form outside the church, exchanging greetings. Several of the men huddled near the front entrance of the church, where they discussed the state of the building. As they leaned backward and tilted their heads upward, they pointed to the big cracks in the stone walls that extended from the foundation to the roof. George, to the surprise of many present, lingered beneath the great old mulberry tree nearby, seemingly uninterested. As the president of the church council, he normally jumped at the chance to join such a discussion, but today he was uncharacteristically aloof.

After a few minutes, the villagers slowly began to disperse. Most took the main cobblestone path that climbed sharply uphill toward the village center. The women and children would continue homeward, while the men would gather in front of George and Thanasis's store.

The summer visitors, mostly former locals now living in Athens, would play cards; talk passionately about politics, hunting, sex, and old feuds; and encourage the elderly among them to spin their yarns about the good old days. The locals, in turn, would want the Athenians to describe all the details of life in the big city—its modern, eccentric customs, the loose women, the amazing spectacles they'd read about in the newspapers.

The discussions would last until one o'clock in the afternoon, at which time they would leave the store and head home for lunch and their customary siesta, eventually lulled to sleep by the drone of cicadas.

CHAPTER 18:
IN THE SHADOW OF PYRGOS

THANASIS WAS THE FIRST TO return to the store that Sunday afternoon after the siesta. He unlocked the door, set the chairs outside around the small metal tables in the courtyard, and waited for the other men from the village to return.

George walked through the door a few minutes later, followed shortly by Panayota and Aggelo.

Before long, Kumes, an energetic young man of twenty, arrived. "George," he said, "may I borrow your gramophone and records for a youth party we're throwing at our home tonight?"

George tugged at his pencil-thin mustache. "Oh, I'm not sure. I might need them myself later."

"Okay," Kumes replied, appearing somewhat crestfallen. He perked back up as he aimed his next question at both George and Panayota. "Anyway, you will join us at the party, won't you?"

"Maybe," George said elusively. "I'll know later."

While Thanasis looked after the store, I spent the afternoon on the move. There were games to be played, and a modest amount of work to be done. The latter included fetching fresh spring water for home and for Thanasis's customers at the store, taking our horse to the spring to drink, and completing small chores around the house for Polyxeni and grandmother, as well as next door for my great-uncle and great-aunt. As was so often the case, I migrated between the store, the village square, and home, never staying anywhere for too long.

By about 6 pm that evening, the oak-covered summit of Pyrgos had begun to cast its long shadow over the village. I watched from our house as the last swarms of bees hurried to their hives in the dappled sunlight. The day, like most in September, had been warm and dry, with temperatures peaking at ninety degrees and everyone in the village scurrying to the shade. Now, with the sun receding, the air was pleasant and mild, though still lacking the slightest trace of humidity. It seemed funny to me that just as the bees were scurrying home, the villagers were beginning to emerge from their houses.

While the children played soccer and hide and seek, some of the grown-ups were watering vegetable gardens from water collection pools made from clay. Others were taking their goats to graze on the low rolling hills surrounding the village.

A few houses away, Panayota had just stopped in on Aggelo. After spotting Aggelo's son Antonakos trying to push himself on a makeshift swing that had been fashioned from a log and plaited grapevine, she rushed to the boy and gave him a hug, followed by two noisy kisses, one on each cheek. At ten years old, Antonakos had reached the age when boys turn their faces away from kissing women, but Panayota quickly won him over by pushing him on the swing, and he was soon giggling with delight.

After Panayota had spent a few minutes with Antonakos, she sat down with Aggelo to share tidbits of gossip and spoon sweets, sweetened fruit preserves served on a spoon.

Several minutes later, she stood up. "I should be going," she said and left for the house.

She could hear the church bell ringing, which meant her husband was summoning the men who were working on the dirt road that was to connect Kupaki with Krokylion, the bigger village to the east. Kumes, with someone else's gramophone tucked under his arm, hurried past, no doubt handing out a few more last-minute invitations to his party.

At the Zakkas house, Panayota joined her sisters-in-law, a couple of her husband's cousins, and the wife of a visitor. The women sat on the front verandah, chatting and watching dusk change the color of the peaks from gold to amber, then purple. It was a familiar-yet-spectacular sight that still gave Panayota goose bumps. While the sun traveled west, the shadow of Pyrgos covered the upper half of the village first, then the church and the school. Once the shadow had advanced further down to the brook, it would creep up the other side, ascending the hill of St. Nicholas like water filling one of the buckets at the village spring. Panayota, like other locals, had seen the ascent of the shadow of Pyrgos so often she could tell time by it—and know how many minutes of daylight remained.

Soon the temperature would fall to roughly sixty degrees, where it would stay for the remainder of the night. Panayota wrapped her arms around her shoulders, anticipating the moment later tonight when, after she had retired to bed, she would pull a blanket up around her neck.

By 8 pm, I had finished playing games and doing my chores and was eating dinner with my brothers and sister and Grandma Efthemia on the covered veranda, which looked out toward the west, now only faintly glowing from the last vestiges of the setting sun. Mother was there. So, too, Aunt Aggelo, who had dropped by for a chat. Father was still working at the store and as usual wouldn't return until much later, after my siblings and I had gone to bed, at which time he and Polyxeni would eat their dinner.

While the grownups talked, night was rapidly falling. Fireflies danced just beyond the light cast from a small oil lamp hanging from a peg on the wall, and somewhere out there in the darkness the many-toned jangling bells of the goats that were being herded back to the village from the hills could be heard, along with a chorus of crickets chirping in the dry grass and frogs croaking from the irrigation pools.

At about half-past eight, Panayota called to us from a pathway that passed above our house. "*Kale orexe!*" she said. "*Bon appétit!*"

She was walking with one of her husband's cousins.

"Come in and have some dinner with us!" Polyxeni called back.

"Thanks," Panayota replied, "but it's getting late. I'd better go. *Kalinikta. Goodnight.*" By the time she got home, the night was pitch black. No moon hung in the sky.

She'd hardly stepped inside, when she heard a sound outside.

One of George's shepherds had stopped at her door on the way to his hut after a game of cards at the village store. "Could I borrow a flashlight?" he asked.

"Sure," she said. A minute later she returned with the only flashlight in the house.

"*Efcharisto,*" the shepherd said, thanking her. "I'll be on my way. *Kalinikta.*"

"*Kalinikta.*"

Around 9 pm, Panayota gazed out the window at the lights beginning to appear on the distant hills, where the shepherds were lighting fires, the flames raging high for a few minutes and then subsiding into smaller flickers of yellow. She had lived in Kupaki long enough to know that mothers all over the village were hustling still-awake children to bed.

"Panayota! Panayota!"

A faint echo from several houses away grew in volume when one of Panayota's neighbors took up the call.

"What is it?" Panayota asked from her doorstep.

"George wants you to go to the Zakkases," the neighbor answered.

"But I just came from there."

"Alexandra says George is staying for dinner. She's asking you to join them."

Panayota shook her head in dismay before trudging over to the neighbor's house, from where she could communicate directly with her sister-in-law.

"I've just come from there, Alexandra!" she hollered. "I've changed into my house robe and haven't got a flashlight!"

Alexandra took a few moments to relay the message to her brother. "George says come as you are for a little while!" she finally hollered back. "It's only us, anyway! Come and have some dinner and some company!"

"I'm afraid to come by myself without a light!" Panayota replied.

Once again there was a pause while Alexandra relayed Panayota's reply to George. "Panayota, George is going to come a little way up by the brook and bring you back so you won't be alone for the darkest part!"

"All right!"

Panayota gingerly descended the cobblestone path that passed above our house. There was still no moon, although the stars were bright, as were the fireflies flitting nearby and the shepherd's fires burning on the distant hills. When she reached the two brooks under the big maple trees, she was enveloped in utter darkness. She could hear music and laughter coming from Kumes's party, just a few houses away.

CHAPTER 19:
FUMBLING IN THE DARK

PANAYOTA WAS RELIEVED TO SEE George's slim silhouette up ahead on the path, where he was waiting for her. He offered his arm, and she gladly accepted it as they walked the darkest stretch of the path, with George pausing every so often to strike a match to illuminate their way. It was at times like this, when George flouted tradition and made his affection for her public, albeit in the darkness, that Panayota appreciated her husband's boldness.

This is his true self, she thought. *If only he could temper his impulses and behave like a gentleman all the time.*

They reached the Zakkas home and sat down for dinner, followed by a smoke. Soon a card game was underway at the dining table.

"Aren't you going to play?" George asked.

"Not tonight," Panayota said and curled up on an armchair nearby. Normally she enjoyed playing cards, but tonight her eyes felt heavy and sleep beckoned.

She drifted off to the noises coming from the youth's party a few houses away. It sounded like a raucous gathering of young people, with dancing, music and plenty of shouting. Panayota could still remember what the village had been like before Nick's dance lessons during the occupation. The older generation had resisted initially, but now dancing was no longer a stolen pleasure but a fashion statement. The tango, the waltz, the fox trot—the young people could do it all. Between outbursts of laughter and cheering, Panayota heard the recorded voices of Zaha, Gunaris, Mendris, and Vempo, among other popular Greek singers. No doubt the partygoers, already light-headed with wine and *ouzo*, were snatching *lukumi*, a gelatinous square-shaped sweet similar to Turkish Delight, from platters as they rested between songs.

George and the others played a couple of rounds of cards

before Panayota roused herself on the armchair. Feeling foggy and uncomfortable, she caught her husband's attention at the table.

"I'm not feeling very well, George," she complained. "Can we go home?"

"George," one of her sisters-in-law said, "you'd better take her home."

"Yes," another chimed in, "she looks really pale."

"In a little while," George said, glancing down at his watch. "Let me just finish this one."

Only a few minutes earlier, the men playing cards and trading stories at the store had finished for the night, and after they left, Thanasis closed up shop. Accompanied by his brother-in-law John Gumas, an Athenian policeman who was vacationing at the village, Thanasis walked slowly up the path toward home. He could hear music being played on a gramophone and echoing from the party next door.

"Would you like to eat with us?" John asked.

"I would," Thanasis said. He made a quick stop home to let Polyxeni know where he was going and then continued on to the Gumas residence, where he ate with John and his mother-in-law, Aggeliki.

"Do you need a light?" Aggeliki asked after he'd had his fill and was ready to go home.

"No," Thanasis answered, "I'll be all right. The starlight is enough for me to see by."

He walked home and found his mother asleep, along with his four children. Polyxeni, meanwhile, had fallen asleep outside on the balcony, no doubt savoring one of the last remaining mild nights of the summer.

"Come to bed, Polyxeni," he said, gently shaking her.

When she didn't respond, he thought better of disturbing her and decided to let her sleep on the balcony. A few moments later, he was lowering his head onto his pillow. Exhausted after a long day's work, he quickly fell asleep.

On any other night, the village would have been quiet by now, save for the crickets chirping and the occasional hoot from an owl or howl from a jackal, barely audible in the distance. Tonight, though, as the clock struck eleven, the youth at their party had switched from what they called "European dancing" to traditional Greek line dancing and the party was still in full swing.

At the Zakkas gathering, meanwhile, and much to Panayota's relief, George appeared finally ready to say goodbye. Their hosts gave them a flashlight, and soon they were walking sharply uphill along the curved path that led toward their home, Panayota walked in front, followed by George with the flashlight.

On this starlit September evening, all of Kupaki reverberated to the racy dance number now blaring from the youth's party gramophone.

The drums they thump!

Thump went a drum.

The drums they boom!

Boom went a deeper drum.

The song, more famous for its rhythm than for its lyrics, now wove the two together.

The drums they thump and boom and boom and thump and boom!

At the party, a young maiden dazzled onlookers as she led the energetic Greek dance called the *Syrto*. Moving in time to the beat, she twisted and turned; leapt effortlessly, her skirt swirling grandly; and then landed lightly on her feet with feline grace.

Thump and boom and boom and thump and—

Boom!

Everyone heard it. Was it part of the music? Some stopped dancing.

Then it came again, this time out of time with the music.

Boom!

The dancers froze. They'd all heard it this time. Someone switched off the gramophone.

"That wasn't a drum!" one of the women said worriedly.

The percussive blast had come from the darkness outside. The partygoers stood still, straining their ears as echoes bounced off the surrounding hills.

"It's a gun!" several said in unison.

The dogs in the neighborhood, smelling fear, suddenly began to howl.

"It was near the ravine!"

"Who can it be?"

"It wasn't from the party, was it?"

I jerked awake and found my younger brother clinging to me. The music we had dozed off to had ceased suddenly, replaced by a jumbled chorus of howling dogs, crying babies, and shouting neighbors. The whole village, it seemed, was in an uproar. "George!" several people hollered from the Zakkas house. "Are you all right?"

"Help!" a man called back. "They are trying to kill us! They are trying to kill us!"

A woman could be heard screaming in agony. "Help!"

I called to my parents. "*Mama! Baba!* What's going on?"

It was the same question my younger brother, still clinging to me, had just asked me, but my parents could offer nothing but uncertainty. We were, each of us, fumbling in the dark.

CHAPTER 20:
"YOU HAVE DEVOURED ME."

"The Nitsoses! Someone murdered the Nitsoses!"

As my parents raced out, they could hear several villagers calling out in confusion. A tangle of voices, distraught and disoriented, echoed in the darkness. Lanterns cast glowing shafts of light as the Zakkases and the partygoers from the Kumes' bash converged on the Gumas residence.

There, in his front yard, John Gumas was lowering a screaming Panayota to the ground. He gently propped her up against a stone wall. The light from a kerosene lantern exposed blood flowing in rivulets from between Panayota's legs downhill toward the middle of the yard. She appeared to have been shot in the chest or abdomen—Thanasis couldn't quite tell.

George, who was able to walk, had just been helped into the yard and was staring at the gathering crowd with dazed eyes. "They have killed us tonight!" he said, repeating the phrase several times in disbelief.

In fact, aside from a few superficial wounds, George looked to Thanasis to be largely unscathed. Two tiny rips in his pants showed near his left knee, plus another a few inches lower, as if he had walked through one of the thorny thickets nearby. There was no blood to speak of, and he was able to walk freely.

"Panayota!" Polyxeni rushed to Panayota's side and began cradling her head, which was lolling from side to side.

"Oh, Polyxeni," Panayota moaned, her voice growing hoarse, "they've killed me! They've killed me!"

"How did this happen? Who did this to her?" Polyxeni looked around wildly at the villagers gathering in the yard.

Thanasis, overwhelmed by rage and despair, clenched his fists repeatedly as he stood next to Polyxeni.

Panayota stared up at him with pleading eyes. "Thanasis," she said, weeping in pain, "they have killed me. Do you think Vasilios has killed me?"

Vasilios, the man whose job George had handed to Socrates, the man whose teenage daughters George had coveted, certainly had reason to hate George Nitsos, but Thanasis knew he wasn't responsible for tonight's shooting.

"No!" he snapped. "It wasn't Vasilios! I told you who would kill you!"

He was furious. Furious at his cousin for ignoring his warnings. Furious at himself for not doing more to protect her. Furious at the man he knew was behind this. Thanasis could hardly look at George, whose mere presence filled him with bitterness.

George's sisters, now crouched beside Panayota, were trying to make her more comfortable by rubbing her arms and placing pillows beneath her head.

"A doctor!" someone shouted. "Get a doctor!"

The words galvanized Thanasis into action, and soon he was barking orders like an army captain. Horses were saddled. Men were dispatched to summon the doctor and the police.

"Mama. Mama." Panayota's voice was feeble now.

"Someone get Papaskevi, Panayota's mother," said a teacher of philosophy vacationing at the village. "And Papazois."

The teacher had just uttered aloud what Thanasis—and likely everyone else standing in the Gumases' yard—was thinking. Expert medical help at such short notice was all but unavailable in remote Kupaki. Although the others were fighting to keep her alive, Thanasis knew Panayota was dying. Peroxide and hastily assembled bandages were a poor substitute for life-saving care.

A priest, on the other hand, was readily available. Summoning Papazois to administer Holy Communion was not only the prudent thing to do, but also their solemn duty as good Christians.

George, meanwhile, walked inside and asked Aggeliki Gumas to make him coffee. "And make it real coffee," he said. "I don't drink coffee with chicory."

He then returned to the courtyard and knelt beside his wife. "Panayota, oh my Panayota," he murmured. "Why you? Why you?"

One of his cousins was rubbing his leg, where the two small rips in his pants were visible.

"Rub him," Thanasis muttered as he paced past George. "That's right. Rub him. A rubbing is what he needs now."

What he really needed, Thanasis thought, was a bullet. Immersed in increasingly dark thoughts, Thanasis barely heard Basil when he approached him.

"Thanasis," Basil said, "we need to phone the doctor in Krokylion."

The only telephone in Kupaki was in the village store. Basil, the kind attorney who had urged patience after my older brother and his friend had been accused of stealing money from the store, was once again offering wise counsel.

"Come with me," the attorney said. "Let's go quickly."

Thanasis followed him from the courtyard and into the darkness. But after only walking a few feet, he stopped dead in his tracks. It was too late for a doctor—he knew that. But it wasn't too late to punish George for what he had done.

"What's the matter?" Basil asked.

"He killed her," Thanasis said through gritted teeth.

"Who killed whom? Who are you talking about?"

"Him," Thanasis answered. "Linatsas. He killed her."

"You mean George killed Panayota?" Basil appeared dumbstruck. "Thanasis, Panayota is still alive, and she might not die if we get on with it and get the doctor here. You're upset. You're forgetting that George was shot, too."

"Exactly," Thanasis said. "He killed her. The scheming bastard got someone to kill Panayota."

"Do you realize what you're saying?"

"I'm going to get my gun and blow his brains out."

"Look here, Thanasis," Basil said, adopting the tone of a cautious lawyer, "if what you're saying is right, it's a matter for the police. Leave it to them."

"He's been trying to get her killed for ages. I know this for a fact."

Thanasis was shaken from his rage when Basil grabbed him assertively by the shoulders. "What in God's name are you trying to do, Thanasis? If you don't care for yourself, at least think of your four children. What will happen to them if their father spends the rest of his life behind bars? So just stop this nonsense, and let's go and phone the doctor."

They walked silently for a while, Basil's flashlight revealing the narrow path ahead of them. Soon they were joined by Alekos Tsipras, a professor of literature and Polyxeni's cousin, who was rushing toward the Gumas house and had been coming from the opposite direction.

Thanasis said nothing and hardly noticed when Basil stopped to exchange urgent words with the professor. He continued on toward home, leaving the two men behind.

"I'm going to get the keys to the store," he muttered.

The errand took only a couple of minutes, and soon he was returning on the same path where he had left Alekos and Basil, who were in the midst of an animated conversation. Basil tried to silence Alekos as soon as they spotted him.

"What did you bring from your house, Thanasis?" Alekos asked sternly. "Show me."

Thanasis produced the keys. He was still livid, but he had left his gun at home.

By the time the three men returned to the Gumas courtyard, two young village men had left on horseback. Their first mission was to instruct Papazois to come to Panayota. Their second was to continue on to Krokylion, the bigger village, to fetch the doctor and the police.

Panayota, her eyes rolling and her face growing paler by the second, was fast losing consciousness as she lay bleeding on the ground. It was doubtful she felt the presence of Alexandra beside her.

"My little bird," said her sister-in-law Alexandra softly, "It won't be long now. The doctor is coming. He's going to make you better, and you'll be up again in no time. You'll see. Everything's going to be all right."

Panayota half-opened her eyes and tried to speak, but no words came forth at first. With great effort, she raised her head. Every ounce of strength she had left was spent whispering something to Alexandra. She then fell back, dead before her head hit the ground.

"What did she say?" someone whispered.

"'You have devoured me,'" someone else answered.

Her remark, difficult to understand in any language other than Greek, meant two things: Panayota felt she had been killed like a gazelle being devoured by a lion, and she was attributing her violent death not to Alexandra in particular but to her sister-in-law's family. In other words, she finally understood what Thanasis had been telling her all along—that George had been conspiring to murder her.

Thanasis noticed that the villagers who had gathered in the courtyard were eyeing with suspicion Vasilios, who had just arrived.

Vasilios, though, seemed unaware of the attention directed his way. He was focused keenly on Panayota, helping solicitously with all that was being done for her.

Just then her mother arrived in the courtyard. "Let me get to her!" she cried. "Let me get to my child!"

Thanasis and the others parted to make way for Paraskevi, and she hurried to her daughter, now motionless and lying still in a pool of her own blood, her lifeless body crumpled in a heap at the foot of the stone wall.

Thanasis's sister Aggelo held Paraskevi as she knelt down beside her daughter, no doubt hoping to help in some way.

The old lady shook off all the helping hands and grabbed her daughter by the shoulders, pulling her up into a sitting position. "Get up!" she shouted. "Get up, you!" She shook Panayota's body. "Breathe! Breathe! For God's sake, breathe!"

She finally loosened her grip on her daughter, and Panayota's body fell back against the ground with a sickening thud. The grief-stricken Paraskevi then tore at her clothes and rolled on the dirt next to her dead daughter.

As he looked away from the spectacle, Thanasis caught sight of his sister moving her hands to her ears to shut out Paraskevi's pitiful wail.

We were still tucked into our bed when the church bells started ringing and several people outside were talking and hurrying along the path beside our house. Soon afterward this commotion, Aunt Aggelo entered with my cousin Antonakos. My brothers and I dashed to them. Nearly two hours had passed since Mother and Father had rushed outside to find out what was happening.

"Aunt Aggelo!" I said. "Where is *Baba? Mama? Giagia?*"

"Your parents and your grandmother have gone to the Nitsoses house," our aunt answered calmly. "Children, go back to bed. Lukas, you and Antonakos can sleep in your parents' bed. Kostas and Panos can sleep in the children's bed. Now get into bed, all of you."

We did as we were told.

"Look," she said while tucking in my cousin and me, "I've got to go. All of you stay here and get some sleep. It's still early."

As soon as she left, Antonakos and I disappeared under the covers, making sure to tuck them in on all sides so there were no cracks and no danger could reach us.

"Aunt Panayota is dead," Antonakos said. "They took her dead body on a cot to the Nitsoses' house." Two years older than me, he spoke with an air of authority. "Vasilios killed her."

"Now they will get him," I offered.

I had heard my father speak about Vasilios before, but never in a flattering way. Some in our family speculated that Vasilios had been the informer who had led the Nationalists to our relative who was killed during the civil war.

The heat from the blankets over our heads was nearly suffocating, but we didn't dare throw them off, for fear of what lay out there in the dark. If someone as beloved as Aunt Panayota could be murdered, we worried that no one was safe.

CHAPTER 21:
A JOB FOR THE POLICE

I WOKE UP THE NEXT morning to find Antonakos still asleep beside me in my parents' bed. But he didn't stay there for long. Aunt Aggelo entered quietly a few minutes later and carried him away without waking him. Afraid to be alone, I crept into the other bedroom where my siblings slept and squeezed myself between them.

My parents finally returned at seven o'clock, well after sunrise, but Thanasis didn't stay long. Polyxeni followed him like a shadow, watching his every move, until he finally rode off toward the direction of the family fields in Maraveli. Then she came back inside and met my gaze.

"Where did *Baba* go?" I demanded. I couldn't understand why she looked so apprehensive. He went to the fields nearly every day.

"Maraveli," she answered matter-of-factly. "Now come and help me."

She was already getting breakfast ready for the children, the rest of whom were still asleep. She paused a moment and then walked absentmindedly toward the balcony, from where we were able to catch a glimpse of Father coming into view below the village cemetery to the south.

The verger was ringing the bell again at St. George. As the last solemn echo died out, I resumed my interrogation.

"*Mama*, did Aunt Panayota die?"

Polyxeni hesitated. "Yes," she finally said, "she did."

"The bastard Vasilios has killer her, *Mama*," I said, assuming the voice of someone well-informed on such matters. "Now he'll see what the police will do to him."

Polyxeni frowned. "I don't want you to repeat that—ever. The police will find out what there is to find out, and they'll deal with it.

All right? Now be a good boy and go to the spring and get me some water."

I grabbed a metal bucket and started up the path toward the spring, coming closer to a policeman who was guarding the murder site. "No, no, not this way," he said, holding up both hands. "Go back," he ordered. "Back! Back!"

I reversed directions and started walking through my family's fields but I found another policeman standing guard. After making another detour to avoid him, I managed to reach the Gumas's house, which had served as a second sanctuary of sorts for me. Whenever I was in trouble for fighting with one of my brothers or for firing my slingshot at something I wasn't supposed to shoot, I retreated there where I was always welcomed by my maternal grandmother.

The courtyard was utterly still. Part of the wall above the sloping yard looked as if it had been scrubbed clean and stood out from the dusty remainder. Below the wall was a moist patch in the dirt, fast drying up, including a tiny red stain that someone had missed. No doubt hearing my footsteps on the path, my Uncle John Gumas emerged from the house to greet me. He seemed to have aged overnight and moved with slow shuffling steps to a stool in the yard. I watched as his head drooped in fatigue, only to suddenly snap up as he spied something on his feet. He hurried inside and then returned a moment later with a pitcher of water, and I suddenly realized what he'd noticed.

"Lukas," he said, his words slurring with fatigue, "pour this for me, will you?"

I emptied the pitcher over his feet, my hands shaking, too afraid to ask whose dried blood I was washing away.

View from the church up.

1. Zakkas 2. Gumas 3. Konandreas 4. Nitsos 5/6. Central square and
Kumes (party house) 7. Pyrgos Hill * Murder site + Gumas Yard

As Thanasis rode into Maraveli, he felt a sense of homecoming. He had spent his childhood in Maraveli, working in the fields or shepherding the family's flock. From the brow of a hill that overlooked his fields, he spotted his old hut. He had walked this same path twice a day while a child: first on his way to elementary school and later on his return home to Maraveli in the evening.

It felt good to be alone. Polyxeni had been hovering worriedly over him since last night. He assumed she'd spoken with Basil or Alekos, either of whom could have told her about his outburst last night. He had cooled down considerably since then and had no intention of blowing George's brains out. In fact, he'd already seen the local police chief, who had set up next door to George Nitsos's house. Thanasis had been the first to present himself in the early morning. During the meeting, which had been guarded, he had inquired about the impending arrival of the captain of the county police. He'd said little else, for he had no wish to tip his hand to the chief, a friend of George's.

Within ten minutes, he arrived at the Panaitakis and Mary's field and, after dismounting, walked to the threshing floor of their hut, where he saw the couple sitting with their backs against a stone wall. Piles of corn kernels sat in front of them.

They looked surprised by his appearance and exchanged glances before standing up to greet him.

"*Kali mera*, Thanasis!" Panaitakis said. "What brings you our way?"

Thanasis swallowed twice. "That bastard killed her last night," he said at last. "It's happened. You told me this would happen, and now it's happened. And I couldn't do anything to stop it!"

Panaitakis's jaw fell open. "Linatsas," he whispered. It was a statement, not a question.

"Yes! And I'm here to ask you what you're prepared to do for Panayota," Thanasis responded. "Will you tell people what he said he would do?"

"When did this happen?" Panaitakis asked, ignoring his question. "Where?"

"At the brook, next to the Gumas house last night as they were walking back home from the Zakkases."

"Did he do it himself, or did he find someone?" Panaitakis asked.

"No, somebody else did it. Nobody knows who. I'm here to ask you what you will do now. Are you going to let everyone know that he tried to hire you to kill her because I'm going to give your name to the police, and they might ask you directly."

"We will," Panaitakis answered. "Of course we will."

Thanasis, exhausted to the bone, nodded and turned on his heels. There was nothing more to say for the moment. He returned to his mare and, after hoisting himself up into the saddle, was on his way.

Thanasis returned from Maraveli by nine o'clock that morning, and Mother once again began shadowing him.

"Go and play somewhere else," she told us.

We watched as she and Thanasis spoke in whispers, eventually moving their conversation to their bedroom. When they came out a few minutes later, they both seemed changed. Mother was no longer warily following him everywhere he went, and he was suddenly more attentive to the rest of us.

"*Baba*," I began tentatively, "who killed Aunt Panayota?"

He did not reply.

"*Baba*, are the police going to arrest Vasilios?"

Father finally looked down at me. "No."

"He killed her, didn't he?" I wasn't happy with my father's taciturn mood and was determined to get an explanation.

"Listen," he said, "your mother told you already that they will not arrest Vasilios. I don't want you to repeat that, all right? It is not your job to find out who killed her. It's a job for the police."

With that, he got up and left the room.

CHAPTER 22:
THE POLICE WANT YOU

LATER THAT MORNING, WE NOTICED everyone in the village assembling in the front yard of the house, which was next to George's house. Word soon spread that the captain of the county police had arrived in the village and was gathering everyone so he could issue a statement.

"We are here to find out what happened," he said, leaning against a window ledge, his hands gripping the ledge and his arms bent backward at the elbows. "And find out we will. In fact, we already know a few things. We're going to arrest the murderer. He's probably amongst you as I speak."

"In this process," he continued, "we may arrest somebody who is innocent but whom we have reason to suspect. I don't want tongues to wag. I don't want you to accuse anybody. I want you to take care of your work and families as before. But don't go far away from the village without permission from the police. Come when we call you or if you have something to report."

Then the captain ordered his men to collect all the shotguns in the village. Soon various villagers were arriving next to the Nitsoses' house, accompanied by one of the captain's men, and presenting their shotguns for inspection. Socrates Karaiskos was the last to bring his weapon, and the wait was made more interesting when rumors began to circulate that he'd hidden his shotgun in a bush before finally retrieving it.

Just then one of the men said that a major from the State Police, was on his way to our village.

"Another policeman?" George Nitsos complained. "What do we need another policeman here for? Why can't this lot here get on with their job?"

111

Most of the villagers merely stopped in for a few minutes to pay their respects, but some never left Panayota's side.

Efthemia, my paternal grandmother, was standing beside the casket and swaying unsteadily.

George Nitsos was quick to offer her a chair.

"Now that you have taken care of everything," Grandma Efthemia replied coldly, "all that is left is to get me a chair."

George stepped back in confusion and retreated into the next room leaving me to wonder what my grandmother could have meant.

At about half past one, the state police major arrived in Kupaki and ordered his men to move to the village school and conduct any interviews or interrogations there.

Thanasis was the first of the villagers to show up at the school and give a statement. After waiting at a student desk in the big hall, he was escorted into the teacher's room, which had been converted into what the villagers would soon be calling an interrogation chamber.

The local police chief introduced him to the county police captain. "Thanasis Konandreas, partner of George Nitsos," the local police chief said. "He would speak only to you."

"Well, I'm here now," the captain said, "and you may speak to me."

Thanasis didn't waste any time on pleasantries. "George Nitsos murdered Panayota," he said and proceeded to give the chief of police the names of a few villagers. "He asked all of these people to kill her, but they refused. I know Nitsos didn't fire the shots and that he himself was wounded. But I think one of these men might have done it."

He then listed a handful of potential henchmen, including Socrates Karaiskos, George's right-hand man.

"Interesting," said the captain. "And I take it you don't think, as many in Kupaki do, that Vasilios shot the Nitsoses."

"That's correct," Thanasis said. "Vasilios is just someone with whom Nitsos has been cultivating a feud in order to point the finger at him when the time comes. It's a clever idea of his to lead the investigation away from his own men."

I was home by midafternoon when Polyxeni approached me.

"Lukas," she said, "will you go find out if your grandmother wants something to eat or drink?"

"Okay," I said and trotted out the door.

I didn't think much about the request until I entered the viewing room and was instantly overwhelmed by the violent stench of rotting flesh. The early afternoon heat had had a profound effect on Panayota's fast-decomposing corpse, which had been severely disfigured not only by the multiple abdominal injuries sustained in the shooting but by the autopsy that had followed.

It took me several minutes to stir up the courage to approach Grandma Efthemia, at the moment lost in another of her dirges. When I finally found the nerve to go through with it, I had no choice but to stand beside her and wait until she had finished another round of mourning, and as I stood there waiting in that crowded, oppressively hot room, surrounded by burning candles, I knew I would never forget the horrific stench assaulting my senses. Decades later, I would see my share of death and tragedy as an emergency room physician. But none of my future encounters would wring my insides the way that did.

To this day, I can still smell the all-permeating stench of decomposing flesh—and the various perfumes the women wore in a vain effort to smother it. I can still hear the rising and falling of grief so raw it sounded like it came from beasts, not humans. From that day on, I knew what hell sounded like—and what it smelled like.

When Thanasis asked Socrates Karaiskos to dig a grave for Panayota later that afternoon, several of us kids in the village followed him down the cobblestone path as he walked with a pick and shovel slung over his shoulder downhill toward the cemetery. It would be a brutal job in the afternoon heat, the kind of job only someone with great physical strength and stamina could tackle. Most of the able-bodied men in the village were too overcome with grief to oblige, but Socrates, forever cold and tough, had agreed to it. Like the rest of us, he probably had no idea that Thanasis had reported him to the police only minutes earlier as a possible suspect for Panayota's murder.

When he passed the section of trail where Panayota had been shot the night before, he didn't so much as pause. Soon we were at the cemetery, from where nearly the entire village was visible. The nearest house stood four hundred yards away. It was here that most locals were buried, typically in the same location as their ancestors. As a result, bones and skulls often came up with the earth after the digging began. A pine casket would then be lowered into the six-foot-deep grave, to be covered by a mixture of old bones and earth.

I watched with both curiosity and dread as Socrates, sweating profusely under the sun, reached a depth of roughly three feet, at which point his shovel began to fill up with old bones, as well as dirt. Availing himself of the age-old gravedigger's humor that helps a person cope with such work, he tossed a few pieces from old skeletons toward us.

We took off in headlong flight, screaming all the way, but stopped after only a few feet and returned. Sheepish, but giggling with the thrill that accompanied our fright, we bolted once more when Socrates hurled more bones our way.

As he continued to dig, Socrates began to entertain his young audience with terrifying tales of skeletons and ghosts. He told us about voices he heard in the remote hills when he was alone tending to his sheep. And we stayed on, preferring his ghoulish fantasies and the levity that unaccountably accompanied them to the real-life gloom that had overtaken our village.

At about half past five, a man shouted for Socrates from the village, his voice echoing off the surrounding hills. "Come here! The police want you!"

The voice, despite the attendant echoes, was easily understood.

"What did you say?" Socrates hollered back.

This time the voice was louder. "The police want you to come here!"

Socrates's already swarthy complexion darkened as he climbed the mountain of freshly excavated dirt next to Panayota's grave, the soft earth giving way while the old bones cracked beneath his boots. He was now towering over us children and facing the village as he cupped his ears in an effort to make out what the man was saying.

"He says the police want you!" a few of the kids dared to say.

He swallowed awkwardly and with apparent difficulty, clearly dehydrated.

"The police need you!" we screamed again in unison.

Socrates cupped his mouth to relay a message to the village. "They want to talk to me?" he shouted. "What for? I'm busy here!"

"They want to talk to you!" came the reply.

"Who wants to talk to me?"

Once again, we answered as a chorus. "The police!"

Finally convinced it was time to leave, he shouldered his tools and walked back to the village, and we followed. The scene could have belonged to the New Testament, with Socrates posing as Christ, and the rest of us playing the part of his beloved children. Reality took a different route, however, when Socrates was interrogated and forced to spend the night at the school's apothiki, a temporary jail, along with two other suspects, both men Thanasis had named. Socrates's gun, we soon found out, was the only one in the village that smelled of powder, indicating that it was the only one recently fired.

That night I had a nightmare about wandering outside in the dark near the brook. In my dream, skeletons rattled after me, each one armed and firing a shotgun, the barrels of their guns spitting fire and hurling deafening blasts at me. Though my parents did their best to comfort me, the nightmares went on every night for nearly a week before finally ending as abruptly as they had begun.

CHAPTER 23:
A VILLAGE DIVIDED

JUST BEFORE NOON ON TUESDAY, less than forty-eight hours after Panayota's murder, the belfry at St. George came alive with the solemn tones of church bells. We were being summoned to Panayota's funeral procession.

As the villagers left their houses and began to gather out front of the Nitsos house, Panayota's mother continued to wail incessantly for her daughter.

An eight-year-old classmate of mine was also crying. She was George's niece, and she wept outside the school building where her father was being detained. Her cries gnawed at me.

"*Baba, Baba,*" she wept, "come home."

Her father was being detained because Thanasis had named him as a suspect. Fortunately, he and another man Thanasis had fingered for the murder would soon be released. The police were slowly narrowing their focus to two men: George Nitsos and Socrates Karaiskos. The predictable result was that our village was being divided into two camps: those that were certain George was guilty, and those who, because of blood relations or close friendship, did not want to believe it.

After the service at the village's church, the procession moved on to the cemetery looping around the policemen who were guarding the school. Through the large window of the school hall, I caught a glimpse of the interior. George, who was not given permission by the police to join the convoy, was sitting with his head on a desk slumped over like an old dog.

We continued through the vineyards, leaving behind one of Kupaki's richest and most powerful men in captivity inside the school. The irony of the situation must have been too much for Eudokia, a cousin of George's, who spoke up halfway to the cemetery. Thin, talkative and ethical, Eudokia was fiercely loyal to her cousin.

"To hell with all those who say George did it!" she burst out. "George loved Panayota. He could never kill her. Never! Never!"

Following the burial, the villagers dispersed quickly, no longer willing to contend with the hot early afternoon sun. But they did so in two distinct groups, each whispering amongst themselves as they walked back to the village. One group consisted largely of the families and close friends of George and Socrates. The other, bigger by far, was made up of the rest of the villagers, most of whom had already tried George and Socrates in their minds and had doled out their punishment: ostracism.

Not long after the burial, Socrates appeared outside the school with several policemen guarding him. He was asked to fire several shots into the ground with his gun. Afterward, rumors began to circulate that the police, with their special investigative tools, had been able to confirm that Socrates's shells matched the one found at the murder scene.

I had always looked up to George Nitsos. Slender, handsome, charismatic, he was the embodiment of power. Over the years, he'd worn many uniforms, whether for the civil government or the military, and he'd always worn them like a second skin, like he belonged at the top. Socrates Karaiskos, too, had long been the object of my boyhood veneration. If George was the brains between them, Socrates was the brawn. Lean but muscular, he was stronger than anyone in the village. He was the man with the gun, a reputation he had built from the days of the civil war and later as a hunter. His steely eyes and deadly aim were at once awesome and intimidating.

But the day after the funeral, as I watched three policemen remove both men from the school and start them on the trail that led out of the village, I couldn't help noticing how suddenly puny they looked.

"They are taking them to jail!" my friends said excitedly, not caring if the two prisoners heard them or not. "They are taking them to jail in Krokylion!"

Papadia, Papazois's wife, was comforting her Aunt Paraskevi on the front stoop when the entourage passed the Soulias house.

"You must tell them what you think of them," Papadia urged her impatiently. "Curse them for stealing your beautiful daughter."

But Paraskevi, timid by nature and undoubtedly hoarse from wailing for nearly three days straight, said nothing.

The procession was nearly out of earshot when Papadia took it upon herself to give the alleged killers a rude farewell. "I curse you both!" she screamed shrilly, her voice easily loud enough to reach the surrounding hills. "I hope you rot where they're taking you. Never come back!"

George and Socrates continued on the trail toward the ragged horizon, and as they slowly made their way along the dusty path, I felt a strange mixture of happiness and disillusionment. On the one hand, I was glad to see Aunt Panayota's killers being taken away. But on the other hand, I had lost more than my aunt; I had lost a hero in George Nitsos, who had always been kind to me and appreciative of my help at the store. He encouraged me to be a doctor, promising help in the process. I wished vainly that I could somehow rewrite history so that Panayota had survived and Vasilios had been responsible for the shooting and dragged away.

View of Kupaki from the hill over St. Antony's Cemetery.

1. Church of St. George 2. School 3. Zakkas 4. Hill hiding the Goumas House 5. Konandreas 6. Nitsos 7. Soulias 8. Central Square 9. Kumes, Party House

Thursday morning, four days after Panayota's murder, Thanasis met with two of George's relatives, along with Papazois and another man, to prepare an inventory of the store. Now that the two business partners were avowed enemies, it was only logical that their assets should be split. With George in jail, and with Papazois overseeing the process, the split was amicable enough.

With that chore behind him, Thanasis rode to Krokylion, and visited the police station to check on the arrested men. He then traveled the next day to Amfissa, the prefecture's capital, where he hired an attorney named Kokkinos.

Then he visited the police headquarters and briefly spoke to the state police major who had come to Kupaki only days before to investigate.

There Thanasis learned that George and Socrates had been allowed to sleep in the same cell in Krokylion the night before.

"That would give them a chance to rehearse their stories," he muttered. "I know this is something the police aren't supposed to do. It just shows that I was right all along about that local police chief. I'm glad I didn't talk to him about my suspicions."

Back in Kupaki that night, Thanasis made an appearance at his store and proudly shared with everyone on hand the optimistic picture that Kokkinos and the state police major had painted for him. While spelling out the details of his meeting, he noticed that many of the usual faces were conspicuously absent. The relatives and friends of George and Socrates, most of whom lived in the upper part of the village, had begun to patronize a smaller store in the village. Kupaki would only grow more divided in the coming weeks and months.

Not long afterward, we were picking corn at out fields with the Panaitakis and Mary helping my parents trying to catch up with the harvest. I did my part by bringing fresh drinking water in a pot from the local spring. I followed the adults from terrace to terrace as they filled their aprons with ears of corn and then emptied them into burlap bags.

"Better dead than divorced, Panayota," Mary said, quoting my murdered aunt. "Better dead than divorced."

"Better dead than divorced," the others repeated.

Many women in the village had begun to remember things that

Panayota had said and done, often launching into a fresh round of tears.

It was mid-September now, and the days were growing cooler. The nights, meanwhile, were longer, which only played into my fear of darkness, which seemed more acute since Panayota's murder.

Every night, as soon as darkness fell, the Nitsoses' dogs, missing their masters, would race over to the brook where their mistress had been shot and began the most pitiful howling, often not stopping until dawn. Although the Nitsoses' doors had been locked and the yard gate sealed, their dogs hadn't given up on the hope that Panayota would someday come home. With our bedrooms facing the opposite side of the brook, there was little we could do to escape the noise. The barking was worse for our neighbors who lived directly next door with their bedroom facing the brook. The dogs maintained their vigil until Panayota's memorial service, which Papazois presided over at the church forty days after the murder.

"Panayota's spirit was unhappy," the neighbors said. "That made the dogs unhappy, too."

One morning in late September 1953, Polyxeni was returning home from the Motsu spring, carrying a pitcher of fresh water on her shoulder. The steep hill and the weight of the water made the going slow, and she stopped behind the Karaiskos house to put the pitcher down and catch her breath. She was just about to continue on when she heard the sound of horses approaching from the village square. A moment later, several policemen appeared, escorting Socrates, who was on foot, and George, who followed on a horse.

Polyxeni, standing with her hands on her hips and staring at him accusingly, caught George's eye. "Why did you do it?" she demanded. "What did that woman do to you to be sent to the cemetery?"

George said nothing and instead fixed his eyes on the mane of his horse as the procession continued along the path toward the murder scene.

Soon word circulated that the police had come to our village in order to reenact the murder.

When the reenactment was over and the investigators were

scribbling down notes on their pads, the police seemed to relax a bit and asked us to fetch them some water.

I took them a pitcher, while others brought water to George and Socrates.

Moments later, George, holding a glass, approached me. "Hello, friend," he said.

I ignored his greeting.

"How are you, my friend?" he continued, undeterred by my silence. "Has school started?"

I stared silently at the man who I was certain had killed Aunt Panayota.

George Nitsos, dashing and charismatic leader of men, fumbled for something to say. Gone was the self-assurance, the charm. Never before had he looked so at a loss for words.

He glanced around uncomfortably, as if searching for an escape route. "I'll help you become a doctor when you grow up," he said softly. It was a familiar phrase, often repeated in the good old days when I had looked up to him with nothing but admiration. Now the words were spoken just above a whisper.

The idea of becoming a doctor certainly appealed to me, but I could no longer take pleasure in George's friendly banter.

I turned on my heels and walked away, George's voice growing faint behind me.

CHAPTER 24:
A CHECK FROM AUSTRALIA

"WHAT DOES IT SAY?" POLYXENI asked Thanasis as he set down the letter from Kutras, his older brother living in America.

With the arrival of October, the villagers had been busily plowing their fields, collecting chestnuts and walnuts, and finishing repairs to their roofs before the autumn rains. Polyxeni, though, fretted that her husband had taken on too much with the trial. Now he was staring off into space, his mind clearly somewhere else, as they sat together at the kitchen table.

"Kutras is in trouble."

"What kind of trouble?"

Thanasis shook his head as he handed Polyxeni the letter. "Read it."

Kutras, who had gone against his parents' wishes and left for America in 1916 at the tender age of fifteen, had been among the million young Greeks to emigrate there during that decade. He was currently running a saloon, the Potter Street Bar, on 600 Potter Street in Saginaw, a city of nearly 100,000 people about ninety miles north of Detroit, Michigan.

As Polyxeni read his letter, she was shocked to learn that he had been stabbed in the chest by a troublemaker at his bar less than a month before Panayota's murder. Worse still, he had been arrested for shooting and killing the attacker. He had later been released, but his legal expenses, combined with his decision to sell his bar and move to Flint in order to ensure his safety, had left him just shy of destitute.

Polixeni felt numb. First it was Panayota's loss. Second, Kutras's misfortunes. In addition, she was recently concerned about her husband's safety.

The families of George and Socrates had been telling the other villagers that Thanasis had gone too far and had better watch out. Was it safe, Polyxeni wondered, for her husband to travel alone to other villages and towns? Often he was delayed on his legal trips, which always made her nervous.

Polyxeni wasn't the only one worried about Father. Grandma Efthemia, too, was watching out for him—and asked me to be her eyes and ears when she couldn't be near.

"Lukas," she said one morning, "I want you to be with your father when he locks up the store at night. Can you do that for me?"

"Yes, Grandma," I answered proudly. It felt good to be recognized as being capable of meeting such a responsibility.

"And walk home with him afterward?"

I nodded in the affirmative once again.

At the store, men, most of them older, were gathering to talk and play cards. They sat on straw chairs and were slouched around round metal tables. Several community announcements hung by tacks from the smoke-jaundiced walls, which had been whitewashed years before. A wood-burning stove, in the middle of the store, provided the heat. Other than a counter and a few shelves stocked with goods, the only other item of interest was a battery-charged telephone, which was mounted on one of the walls.

Along with selling cigarettes, groceries, and other merchandise to the customers, I brought playing cards to the men and prepared their drinks. Worry beads softly ticked against one another as cards hit the table with a competitive thump, backgammon sets clattered, and stories were told about George and Socrates in years gone by and wars in which the men had fought and travels they had made to America and other faraway lands.

As the murder investigation continued, our teacher, encouraged us to concentrate on our schoolwork.

"Do not get caught up in other matters," he cautioned us one day in class. "You are here to study."

The speculation and verbal exchanges, however, continued in secret.

"They are guilty," a classmate whispered. "They will pay for it."

"You're wrong!" another shot back. "You'll pay for the injustice!"

Soon my classmates and I were solidly divided into two camps: one on George and Socrates's side, and one on Thanasis's. The division in our school was merely a reflection of the village at large. There were those who supported the accused and those who wanted to see them put away for good—or worse. Those in between were few. Of those who pretended to be neutral, many did so only to avoid being dragged into the affair. In their minds and in conversations with those close to them, they held much stronger views.

The very geography of the village conspired to accentuate the rift. In the area in the upper part of the village known as *Nitseika*, or the Nitsos Neighborhood, lived all those who either bore the name Nitsos or were at least related to the Nitsoses in some way. Their neighbors also supported Nitsos, who was popular among them. The central and lower parts of the village, which consisted of about two-thirds of the population, supported Thanasis. While the men from the first group congregated in a smaller village store, those from the latter group frequented our store in the village center. The women from each group, meanwhile, avoided the other side when they went to collect water from the springs or wells. Amongst themselves, though, they sustained a constant news network, supplying each other with the latest information on the murder investigation.

The divide even extended to *Nyhteria*, the nighttime drop-in visits so integral to Greek rural culture. Now when villagers stopped in after dinner to chat, joke, and enjoy chestnuts, feta cheese, and wine around the fire, they did so only amongst families of the same faction. It had become unthinkable to celebrate name days and other occasions with the whole village attending. Sometimes a child would sneak through for a piece of cake, but otherwise the opposing factions kept clear of each other, even at festivities.

Even Papazois struggled to maintain neutrality. The cracks in the church's stone walls were finally about to be repaired, but new fissures were now appearing among the congregation. As a Greek Orthodox priest, Papazois's first inclination was to leave men's affairs to men. But he inevitably began to speak out in support of Thanasis, his brother-in-law, sparking outrage among George and Socrates's supporters.

One night at the store, shortly after the rest of the customers had gone home, Thanasis spoke to one of his childhood friends.

"I got a letter from Panayota's brother," he said.

"From Metsios?" the man answered.

Thanasis nodded and proceeded to read the contents of the letter, which had come all the way from Australia, Metsios's adopted home. "It says, 'I want to thank you for your efforts on behalf of my sister. The cowards responsible for her death must not be allowed to escape justice. I have enclosed a check for one thousand Australian dollars. This is my first contribution to the legal fund. More will follow. Thank you once again, Thanasis, for going after those two *Kiaratades* (cuckolds). Let us hope they are executed or jailed for life. You can count on me to take care of the expenses.'" Thanasis showed his friend the enclosed check.

His friend raised his eyebrows at the princely sum on the check. "Impressive."

His reaction, which fell somewhere between surprise and awe, was heartening, Thanasis thought.

Even more encouraging was the speed with which his friend trumpeted the news. Most, if not all of Panayota's supporters, were cash-strapped. It was likely some would step up to support Thanasis's efforts, despite the fact that they could never match George Nitsos's resources and connections—but only if they saw others doing the same. No one wanted to be on the losing side, and to most in the village, the losing side was the one without money.

Midway through November 1953, Polyxeni, Aunt Aggelo, and Mary were summoned to the public prosecutor's office in Amfissa, where they were expected to give their statements. Thanasis accompanied them to the prosecutor's office and then left to see Kokkinos at his law office.

As Polyxeni and the others waited in the lobby outside the interrogator's office, a middle-aged man approached Mary, and beckoned her to join him in the hallway to discuss something personal. She left the others, but didn't walk far enough to keep their conversation out of earshot, for Mary was hard of hearing and forced the man to speak louder.

Polyxeni, suspecting something was afoot, warily traded glances with Aggelo. She then cocked her head slightly toward Mary and the man talking several feet away. Although she was unable to make out everything said, it sounded like the man was trying to convince Mary to say something to the interrogator. Polyxeni glanced from the two talking furtively in the hallway to her sister-in-law, whose wide-eyed expression suggested she'd heard the same thing.

"Let's tell Thanasis," Aggelo whispered.

When Mary returned, her round face was contorted with tension, worry lines arcing across her forehead.

"I see you have secrets with male friends in the big town, Mary," Aggelo quipped. "An old sweetheart?"

Perfect! Polyxeni thought. Aggelo had managed to pry—but in a lighthearted way.

"That was a man from the village where I was born," Mary fumed. "He was trying to make a deal with me."

"What deal?" Polyxeni and Aggelo asked simultaneously.

"Nitsos must have sent him. He was offering me Nitsos's fields, the house in Kupaki for me and my family to live in for as long as we wish, and all the livestock Nitsos owns in partnership with Thanasis."

Polyxeni shook her head in disgust. "And what did he want in exchange, Mary?" She already knew the answer but felt compelled to confirm her suspicions.

The stout little peasant farmer shrugged her shoulders. "Lie for Nitsos," she said matter-of-factly. She frowned thoughtfully. "I have needs, but he can keep it all. I don't want my soul to burn in hell forever."

"Thank you, Mary," Polyxeni said, touching the woman's shoulder. She didn't know what else to say.

CHAPTER 25:
A PISTOL IN THE POCKET

THANASIS WAS RETURNING FROM HIS fields at dusk one day in late November when he stopped at the village spring for a drink of water. After quenching his thirst, he leaned against a large stone and closed his eyes, the trickling water from the spring and the rustling leaves of the beech trees nearly lulling him to sleep.

A moment later, he opened his eyes to see Eleni, George's sister, standing just a few feet away.

"Hello," she said coolly.

"Hello," he replied.

Suddenly her face burned pomegranate-red, and he could tell she was gathering the courage to say something she knew he didn't want to hear.

"You know my brother is innocent, Thanasis," she said, "and if it's money you're after, just stop going after him. Just drop the case, and we won't let it go unrewarded."

Thanasis locked eyes with her. "You know your brother is *guilty*. I'm not selling the blood Panayota and I shared. You can keep your reward."

Eleni took two steps backwards and then stopped and turned toward Thanasis. "You're not going to be able to touch George!" she screamed. "You might just share Panayota's fate!"

Thanasis opened his mouth to reply, but she scurried away before he could muster a single word.

From that day forward, he began carrying a gun.

"Thanasis," Polyxeni said in an alarmed voice when she spotted it one day, "what on earth is this?"

"It's a gun," he said flatly.

"I know what it is. What's it doing in your coat pocket?"

"There are a lot of foxes and jackals around," he said, groping for an explanation, "more than usual for this time of year. We won't have many sheep left if it goes on like this. Our shepherd and I have been planning to trap and kill a few."

"Hmm," Polyxeni said, clearly not convinced.

A few days later, Papazois got wind of Thanasis's sidearm and gently rebuked him. "Why do you need to carry that gun? Who's threatening you?"

"Who isn't?" Thanasis snapped. "Even Eleni told me the other day I was going to go the way of Panayota."

"She didn't!" Papazois looked genuinely shaken as his brow met beneath his stovepipe hat. "When did this happen?"

"A couple days ago at the spring" Thanasis said. He produced his gun, a black Savage .32-caliber pistol, and regarded it fondly. "Why do you think I carry this?"

"Thanasis, put that away!" Papazois interjected hastily. "Tell me what happened at the spring."

Thanasis rehashed his conversation with Eleni.

But the priest appeared unconvinced. "Don't let your imagination run away with you, Thanasis. She was just upset. It doesn't mean they had your cousin killed or are planning to kill you now."

When Christmas finally came that winter, the village was hardly in a festive mood. After the traditional service, we gathered outside the church to exchange greetings and wish each other a merry Christmas.

Papazois, as usual, was out front shaking hands, but he, like everyone else, looked stiff and uncomfortable. He had asked me to assist him in the customary blessing of the homes in the village, and after we began our rounds in the lower part of the village, I couldn't help noticing the pensive expression on his face, which even his white flowing beard couldn't disguise.

We were halfway up the cobblestone path outside George Nitsos's house when Papazois, appearing lost in thought, jerked to a stop.

Weighed down by all my altar boy paraphernalia, I stumbled into him, unable to stop in time.

"Sorry, *Papuli*," I said, embarrassed.

"It's all right, son," he replied absentmindedly. "My fault." He was staring at the black linen banner, fixed to the balcony railings, which read *PN* (the initials for Panayota Nitsos) in white letters.

Had she still been alive, Panayota would have invited us inside, offering us a warm welcome, music, and plenty of good food to taste. She would have encouraged us to rest before we continued our climb.

Papazois heaved a heavy sigh and then proceeded next door to the home of Nitsos's cousin.

Eudokia and her husband welcomed us inside, and after Papazois had performed the blessing ritual, they invited Papazois to join them for meat, feta cheese, and red wine around the fireplace.

The adults talked a while before Eudokia brought up Panayota's murder. Soon she was weeping for the loss of her neighbor, cousin, and friend.

"As our priest," she asked, wiping away her tears, "what are you going to do for the two innocent people in jail?"

Papazois frowned sympathetically but said nothing. It was clear he had hoped to avoid the subject altogether.

But Eudokia pressed on. "This issue is dividing the village," she said, "and the priest has the moral responsibility to intervene. You need to talk to Thanasis. You must stop this avalanche, or it will lead our village to destruction."

The old priest, no doubt sensing there was no escape, finally offered a reply. "I'm the priest of everybody in Kupaki, Eudokia," he said, carefully weighing his words. "I try not to take sides, but I hear what even George's relatives are saying about this. They openly talk against him and call him a wife murderer."

Eudokia's eyes narrowed angrily.

"Of course," Papazois added, "I take nothing without a pinch of salt, but Panayota is dead. I did not hear her voice next door today. She lies in St. Anthony Cemetery. Somebody has killed her. What do you say to that, Eudokia?"

The mere mention of Panayota's name was enough to send a fresh round of tears streaming down Eudokia's cheeks. Her husband reached over to comfort her.

"I will try to keep an open mind and see what comes of all this," Papazois concluded before standing up. He motioned to me to follow and started toward the small porch.

"Have a good night and many years!" Eudokia called after us. "I'm sure our bishop also will want you to keep an open mind!"

The bishop had a fierce reputation among the priests in his

jurisdiction. Was Eudokia insinuating she would complain to him? Papazois either didn't grasp the thinly veiled threat or simply didn't know how to respond to it. He led me into the cool night air without offering a reply.

Winter came and went, and by mid-May of 1954, the school grounds and adjacent churchyard were teeming with construction laborers hard at work on rebuilding the church's cracked stone walls. My classmates and I participated as did every able man and woman in the village-wide effort.

Basil, the kind and thoughtful uncle of my brother's friend, oversaw the project. As an attorney and notary public, he was uniquely qualified to coordinate the activity, pay the workers, and solve any problems that arose during the construction.

One night Basil visited the store, where Thanasis took the opportunity to approach him about the upcoming trial.

"Would you be willing to testify?" Thanasis asked gingerly. He was certain that testimony from Basil, an educated and reputable man, would be indispensable to the prosecution.

Basil frowned, dropping his head as if to ponder the request. He then took a deep breath and, delaying his response a few seconds longer, cleared his throat. It was obvious that Thanasis's request was something he had expected but nevertheless had been hoping to avoid.

"Thanasis," he finally said, "I don't think you'll need me."

"Not need you?" Thanasis shot back in disbelief. "You're the most important witness!"

"Listen, I've been talking to the police and even to some local judges who are following the case," Basil replied in a reassuring tone. "They all say—and it's my personal opinion, too—that the case against Nitsos and Karaiskos is clear. We all foresee nothing but their conviction, with a sentence of between twenty years and life imprisonment."

"From your mouth to God's ear!" Thanasis crossed himself. "But you know their camp will spend lots of money on the case and that nothing is certain. I really need you, Basil."

"Thanasis, since there are so many witnesses from the village who will testify against Nitsos and Karaiskos, one more won't make much difference. It would be better for me to pretend to be neutral. I can't take sides. If I do, it will affect the work on the church project. You see, I've been trying to get the funds for the repair of the church from Nitsos. I've been talking to some members of his family, asking them to mediate on my behalf."

As church council president, George had control of the church funds. At the moment, he was holding the money allocated for reconstruction, although there was a lawsuit pending against him.

"Basil, you think you can appeal to his conscience through members of his family? It sounds as though you've forgotten who Nitsos is."

Basil, Thanasis realized, was trapped—and unwilling to break loose. There was nothing left to say.

The attorney bid him a goodnight, leaving Thanasis to stew in his own disappointment behind the counter. Thanasis knew that many in the village took his side and regularly cursed Nitsos for holding on to the church construction fund as well as for the fatigue the volunteer workers were suffering. Others mockingly stated that George would be released from jail and not only return the church's money, but also singlehandedly finish the job.

Of course, there were those, mostly relatives and friends, who kept quiet on the issue or were openly defensive. "If you think you're going to find them guilty," they would say, "you're fools."

"But they *are* guilty," others would respond, "are they not?"

George's defenders invariably repeated themselves: "If you think they'll be found guilty, you're fools."

Their certainty left Thanasis feeling uneasy. What did they know that he didn't? Would George find a way out of his predicament? Had he already?

The trial itself wasn't slated to start for several months, not until October 18, but already there was much talk in the village about the witnesses who would be testifying. At home, Thanasis watched Polyxeni turn toward the church and cross herself in disbelief after learning of the witnesses on the defense's list. Efthemia unloosed a litany of curses, while the children echoed their parents' contempt for the process, which already seemed tainted.

Thanasis soon learned that the other side was equally displeased. His sister Aggelo, relating a conversation she'd had with Eudokia, told him that Eudokia and George's other supporters were furious that Papazois would be testifying in court. Papazois was Thanasis's brother-in-law, Eudokia had argued, and couldn't possibly be neutral.

Meanwhile, the latest letter from Metsios in Australia was full of bad news: Metsios's restaurant wasn't doing well and he would no longer be able to contribute money to the legal fund, at least not anytime soon. The letter, like the oppressive heat of May, knocked the wind out of Thanasis. So, too, his wife's reaction. Polyxeni wanted to know how Thanasis was going to pay all the legal fees *and* save money for his children's educations.

A few days later, distracted by financial worries, a heavy-hearted Thanasis went to Athens in order to search for an attorney, to arrange accommodations for the witnesses, and to talk to his brothers-in-law, the Gumases, about a short-term loan so he could pay some of the legal fees. The hiring of an attorney was relatively easy, but when he asked the Gumases, who were renovating their house, about the short-term loan he was met with surprise and skepticism.

"We thought Metsios, Panayota's brother, was going to pay for court expenses, Thanasis," they told him. They pointed to a pile of bricks near the back patio. "Can't you see what a bleeding gash we're trying to sew up here?" Then his two brothers-in-law cautioned Thanasis about his involvement in a case in which the defense was far better financed, something that could potentially influence the court's decision.

"Don't misunderstand us, Thanasis," they said. "We're with you. It's just that we can't afford to help you financially. Look, why don't you use this house for some of the prosecution witnesses from Kupaki to stay in during the trial?"

"*Efcharisto.*" Thanasis forced a smile. "That will be a great help."

CHAPTER 26:
THE SIGNATURE

WHILE THANASIS WAS IN ATHENS, life went on as it always had back home in Kupaki, where the wheat harvest occupied every able-bodied person. Some villagers carried huge loads of the harvested wheat on horseback from the fields to the threshing floors, while others, armed with sledgehammers, crowbars, and machetes, cleared the most difficult terrain: the path between the village and the cemetery. Thick undergrowth needed to be cleared away from a narrow, treacherous path already cluttered with boulders.

Among those sweating beneath the hot sun was Johnny, son of Panaitakis and Mary. He had just set his ax on the ground next to a spring on the edge of the village and was already pouring water into his cupped hands when he spotted George Nitsos's pretty sister, Eleni, walking toward the spring from the Zakkases.

Johnny took a thirsty gulp and then straightened to greet her.

"*Yasu*, Johnny."

"*Yasu*, Eleni," he replied.

"You poor thing," she said in a sympathetic tone. "You look so tired. And what have you been doing to yourself?"

Johnny looked down at his shirt, which was streaked with sweat and was now missing two buttons, and then lower to his work pants, which had been torn by sharp thorns. He then glanced from his rumpled attire to Eleni's innocent, doll-like face.

She smiled at him sweetly. "Why don't you take a break and come to our place for some *ouzo* and *lucumi*?" she offered. "That should cheer you up."

"That sounds nice," Johnny said, unable to resist her kindness—or the offer of a respite.

Inside her home, away from the hot sun and prying eyes, Eleni

133

plied Johnny with cool drinks and refreshment. And somewhere between his second and third glass of *ouzo*, floating in a heady buzz, he absentmindedly signed a blank sheet of paper that she handed to him. He wasn't quite sure why he'd been asked to offer his signature— Eleni said something about needing his support at the upcoming trial—but he knew she and her family had always been kind to him and thought it was the least he could do.

When Thanasis finally returned from Athens, he found the plum trees in our garden weighed down by ripening fruit, their branches nearly touching the ground. Mother, too, looked like she was carrying a heavy burden. There were worry lines on her face that he'd never seen before. In typical fashion, she said nothing of her problems. If he was the loud one in their relationship, she was the proper one, the placid one. She never complained, never raised her voice to her husband. None of the Gumases ever did, but often their silences or their soft-spoken reproaches made a man feel guiltier than if accusations had been shouted at him.

Thanasis, hoping to diffuse the tension, silently thought over how to approach her. She saved him the trouble the next morning as they lay awake in bed.

"Thanasis," she said softly, "do you know you go away these days, saying that you're off to Krokylion and will be back in the evening, and the children and I don't see you again for three or four days? Then we hear from others who saw you in other towns farther away, and they say you're so lost in thought that you don't even see them pass you. This village was the safest place on earth for me before all this happened. Now I live in fear daily, worrying about what is happening to you and what will become of the education of our children when all the money we have been saving is spent in court. Your mother is getting harder and harder to please, and I simply haven't got the time anymore. She shouts, 'Murderers! *Kiaratades!*' whenever she sees any relative of Nitsos or Karaiskos. You know how I detest a scene. To add to all this, my older brother Georges writes such depressing letters from Korea. In his last letter, he says, 'Don't become a widow, little sister. Before it's too late, ask your husband to stay home and end his adventures with the law.'"

Thanasis knew that Georges, an air force officer stationed in a war zone, saw little reason to be hopeful. He was daily experiencing the horrors of the Korean War, which Greece, as a member of the United Nations, had joined.

"Polyxeni," he said tenderly, "four more months—that's all it will take for all our troubles to be over. All our lawyers assure me that it will be a straightforward win for the prosecution. Trust me."

"From your mouth to God's ear, Thanasis!" She crossed herself. "St. George, make that come true."

Thanasis, too, crossed himself, and as he did, he felt a pang of guilt. It had been far too easy to give his wife hope—the very thing he was in danger of losing.

The school year was already behind us by early July, when the vacationers began to arrive at our village. My friends and I chatted excitedly to our Athenian counterparts about the latest in the capital, and soccer matches sprang up suddenly in open fields and courtyards all over Kupaki. Handshakes, hugs, kisses, backslapping, hearty welcomes, lingering farewells—all were the same as usual. The shadow of the murder and impending trial, however, loomed everywhere, unspoken yet ever present.

We had been transformed by Panayota's death and the subsequent divisiveness, no one more so than Papaskevi, her mother. When she opened the door one day, she was shocked to see George Nitsos's sisters standing on her front stoop.

"We won't ask you how you are," Alexandra said. "We know you must be feeling what we all feel—only worse. How can anyone who knew Panayota ever forget her?"

Eleni, standing at Alexandra's side, nodded gravely.

Touched by their sincerity, Paraskevi broke into tears, and the two younger women began consoling her. She invited them inside; hospitality demanded it. Indeed, she couldn't have possibly turned away a friendly visitor on her doorstep, but in her grief she let slip more than one barbed comment about her visitors' brother, instantly regretting each slip of the tongue.

To her surprise and relief, Eleni and Alexandra didn't take offense. Instead, they deposited on her kitchen table several bags containing rice, sugar, coffee, and Turkish delights, among other items.

"*Efcharisto,*" was all she could say as she meekly accepted the gifts. "Thank you".

After the two women departed, Paraskevi told her neighbor and niece about the visit.

"What kind of business did Linatsas's sisters have with you?" Papadia demanded. As Thanasis's sister, it was clear she considered Paraskevi's acceptance of the gifts an affront to all those who had sworn to bring Nitsos to justice. And as Papazois's wife, it was obvious she felt she had the moral right to speak her mind. "They brought you presents and you just accepted them?"

"I didn't want the food, Papadia," a confused Paraskevi replied, determined to defend herself. "But I am too old to learn how to turn people away from my door and spurn kindness with a slap in the face."

"Some people become more and more foolish the older they get!" Papadia muttered on her way out. "The Lord didn't hesitate on the high mountain to tell Satan what to do with his gifts!"

Late one afternoon, just after siesta, Thanasis visited his friend Alekos Tsipras, whose house was a short walk from the store. Alekos, a philosophy teacher, was the one who wanted to see, on the night of the murder, if Thanasis had brought the store key or a gun to kill Nitsos from his house. While Alekos, still groggy from his afternoon nap, washed his face with cool water from his well, Thanasis sat in the shade of a mulberry tree. Soon the two men were joined by some visitors from next-door, and they all sat down to drink coffee. It wasn't long before they were discussing the murder and the upcoming trial. None of the men bothered to lower his voice—or curb his profanity directed at George Nitsos.

The front door of the house next door opened, and Eleftheria, a relative of George's, appeared in her apron. "Says Thanasis Konandreas!" she scolded the men after marching out into her front yard to confront them. "So what is the need for a trial in Greece, eh?"

"Why are you so het up, Eleftheria?" Thanasis retorted. "All the fair-minded people in the village have no doubt they're the murderers."

"The people of the village," Alekos said and motioned to the other men in his front yard, "all of us know it, Eleftheria."

"All I am saying is that you should wait for the court's decision and not be prejudiced," Eleftheria responded. "Thanasis had his trial and was found guilty, and we don't call him a criminal. You call us murderers before the decision."

"Even every single child knows who the murderers are," Alekos snapped. "Even those like you who pretend they don't know. But Eleftheria, please go back inside your house. Don't let's make a scene now."

In August, after celebrating the Repose of the Mother of Christ with a village-wide feast, we said goodbye to the vacationers, who were ready to return to Athens. Their departure, however, was balanced by the arrival of several newcomers to the village. The newcomers liked to visit the brook where Panayota had been murdered, the church, the village square, the general store, and the Nitsos and Zakkas houses. They belonged to two distinct groups, and we could easily tell them apart.

Members of the first group looked sophisticated but austere. They never smiled. They wore neck ties, carried leather handbags bulging with papers, and spoke and were friendly only to a few while treating others with hostility. The village dogs ferociously attacked them from the moment they arrived and didn't let up until they had departed. They were attorneys hired by the defense or the prosecution.

Members of the other group dressed flamboyantly, carried cameras, which hung from their shoulders, and smiled, joked, and spoke with everyone. They even tried to touch and play with the friendlier village dogs after realizing the local girls were beyond their reach. They were journalists from the Athenian dailies, court reporters with a special interest in whatever bits of gossip they could extract from the locals.

PART IV

CHAPTER 27:
TO THE COURT IN ATHENS

ON SUNDAY, OCTOBER 17, 1954, the bus carrying roughly a dozen prosecution witnesses pulled to a stop at the Athens depot, and there waiting near the platform was none other than Thanasis. He welcomed everyone warmly and gave them directions to their lodgings. About eight of them stayed at the Gumases' house, some of them bedding down on floor, where they would sleep for the next week or two while they waited to give their depositions in court.

The next day which was the first day of the trial, Thanasis sat calmly in a small chamber in the courthouse in downtown Athens. Beside him were the other prosecution witnesses, each lost in their own thoughts. Some paced nervously. Others traded small talk to quiet their nerves.

Socrates's handcuffs are removed as George, center, looks on.

Thanasis had gone to court once before and knew well what he was up against. So long as he told the truth, he told himself, he had nothing to fear. In fact, that simple fact gave him great strength. He had only to be his usual, personable self. Nothing less. Nothing more.

The trial had convened just minutes earlier. The courtroom, overflowing with spectators, had buzzed with anticipation before the Judge had finally called the people to order. As policemen had shooed away latecomers too numerous to be seated, the accused—George Nitsos and Socrates Karaiskos—had arrived with their defense team of five attorneys. The jury, ten strong, had already been seated.

"Intentional murder, illegal bearing of weapons, illegal use of weapons..." After the public prosecutor had reeled off the charges, Papaskevi, Panayota's mother, had appeared with her attorneys Kokkinos and Tsukalas, and the judge had addressed the witnesses and ordered them to avoid interviews with the press. He had then directed them to their respective chambers, where they now waited their turn.

Several minutes went by before a bailiff appeared and motioned to Thanasis to follow him back to the courtroom. It was his turn.

Thanasis stood up, straightened his gray-and-white-striped tie, which matched his solemn gray suit, and followed the man into the crowded courtroom, that was now eerily quiet. Walking in the opposite direction was Paraskevi, Panayota's mother—all four feet, two inches of her. It was clear she'd given the court an earful about the defendants. Her grief, still palpable, weighed heavily on everyone. *Kathimerini*, the Athenian daily newspaper, would describe her in the next day's edition as a "biblical figure with a thundering voice and a hawk's eye." At the moment, even the defense appeared at a loss for words after her testimony, against which they'd raised no objections.

Thanasis noticed Palos, the leading defense attorney, giving him a skeptical once-over as he took his place behind the witness stand. He knew the type: cagey, tough, relentless. He was wary of the attorney, but not intimidated.

"Thanasis Konandreas," he rasped, "is it true that you once beat up a man in your village?"

Here we go, Thanasis thought. He had assumed the defense would go after his past. But he had nothing to hide. In fact, the experience had taught him much. At that trial so many years ago, his defense attorney had maintained that no one had spotted him anywhere near the other men who had been beaten. There had been no witnesses. But the court had seen through his attorney's strategy and found him guilty nonetheless. Wiser and older now, he knew truth was on his side this time.

"Yes," he answered matter-of-factly, "that's true."

"And is it true that you served time in jail?" Palos drew out the last four words, making sure no one in the courtroom failed to grasp the importance of what he was saying.

"Yes."

The attorney puffed up with pride at the excited murmuring that followed amongst the spectators. "So let me get this clear," he said. "You assaulted an innocent man and served time for it?"

"No."

"No? You were sure that you served time for assault just a moment ago, and now you're sure you didn't?"

Thanasis knew the attorney was trying to lay a trap for him, but he also knew a way out. He turned to the Judge. "May I explain this?"

"Proceed," the judge said before a clearly surprised Palos could object.

"I spent six months in jail in early 1934," Thanasis began. "My family was targeted by another family that owned property near ours because of property disputes and rumors that a Konandreas man had had a relationship with one of their girls a long time ago. The father of the girl filed several lawsuits against me, falsely accusing me of allowing my livestock to trespass into his fields. I approached him several times and told him that I respected him and his family and that I should not be personally targeted as revenge. Despite my pleas, he remained hostile.

"Then one night I was awoken by my sheepdog barking frantically. I realized that rustlers were trying to steal my sheep. I stepped outside, made a noise as if I was loading a gun, and urged my dog to go and investigate. This must have scared the rustlers away because soon the dog became quiet.

"The next day the girl's family found out that several of their animals were missing. They were clearly taken away by the rustlers, but the family decided that I had directed the whole thing, as other shepherds told them that a commotion was heard in the night near my hut the previous night.I protested my innocence and explained what I knew of the incident. In spite of this, he accused me of rustling and directing rustlers to his flock. Preliminary investigations followed, a matter likely to cost me and my family substantial aggravation and expense.

"One day at our fields in Maraveli, my sheep were near that man's fields, and I went to chase them away before they crossed into his property. He then started stoning me and would not heed my shouts to stop. I had to defend myself and a brawl ensued. I don't quite remember how the fight started. I lost my temper and when I calmed down, I found that, because I was younger and stronger than he was, I had badly beaten him.

"The matter went to court. Though I was cleared of the charge of rustling, I was convicted for assault. This is a matter I am not proud of, and I have always felt regretful about losing my temper, though I was badly provoked."

Thanasis took a deep breath and realized the courtroom had fallen silent once again.

"Counselor," he said, looking directly at Palos, "I made that mistake twenty years ago, and I've paid my debt to society. And this trial is for the murderers of Panayota, not for me."

Palos appeared to swear under his breath, he had underestimated Thanasis.

Thanasis, for his part, knew he still had a long way to go to convince the jury that he was a reliable witness. More questions followed, which he answered calmly and truthfully.

"On September 6, 1953, the day of the murder, the Zakkases did not invite Panayota to dinner when she visited them earlier in the evening," he said, recounting his cousin's last hours. "After leaving the Zakkases, she stopped at a neighbor's on the way home and got some tomatoes for the dinner that she was going to cook. Later, Nitsos got his sisters to ask Panayota to join them for dinner. It's clear that Panayota had no idea this was going to happen since she had given away her flashlight to Pagonis, the shepherd who worked for Nitsos. She was heard telling her sister-in-law that she had just come from them and didn't understand why she should go back again."

Thanasis paused to collect his thoughts. What he was about to reveal to the court was shocking—so shocking that many of the faces staring intently at him would soon be registering wide-eyed disbelief or even disgust.

"Nitsos arrived at the village church next to Katina's house on that day when it was still light outside. When he left, it was still not dark. He reappeared at the Zakkases' only about an hour later—well, not less than half an hour later. During that time, Nitsos had sex with Katina in the open, next to the church."

An incredulous Judge raised his eyebrows. "If, as you say, Nitsos had prior knowledge that his wife was going to be murdered in three or four hours' time," he said, "would he have been in the mood for that?"

"Yes, Your Honor," Thanasis answered. "A selfish and shameless man — shameless to the bone like Nitsos — would be. In my rage, I would have killed him that night," Thanasis continued. "I was going to get my handgun. Basil calmed me down and stopped me."

"How very interesting," the judge said. "So you were going to kill the defendant. Did anybody else persuade you against taking the law into your own hands?"

"Yes," Thanasis answered, looking at the floor. "Tsipras, the philosophy teacher."

"Was Karaiskos a good hunter?" asked the judge.

Thanasis, wondering where this was leading, straightened slightly. "Yes. An ace hunter. I have seen him shoot down a partridge with a rifle from no less than five hundred feet away. I saw this with my own eyes."

"You say that Karaiskos had killed a partridge two days earlier," the defense attorney broke in. "You say that this was to have an explanation ready for the fact that his gun had been recently fired."

"That's right."

"Then could you tell the court why he couldn't have done something less elaborate—like clean his gun?"

"I don't know. Perhaps he didn't think about it."

"Your Honor," Palos said, "the defense has already put it to the court that it has reasonable doubts about the shell that has been submitted by the police as evidence. We hold that it belongs to the bullet from Karaiskos's gun when he was made to fire test shots by the captain of the police and is not, as the prosecution claims, the shell from the gun that was used at the crime scene."

"That's impossible," Thanasis objected. "Even a trainee policeman could not have made such a mistake. The captain—"

"That's enough," the Judge said and gave Thanasis a stern look. "The court will ask if it wants an expert opinion from someone on the police force as witness." He stroked his chin thoughtfully. "Instead of killing his wife, could Nitsos not have divorced her?"

"No, Panayota used to threaten Nitsos that she would kill him if he divorced her. Nitsos was afraid. He would have known that she wouldn't go that far, but he would have also known that she would make his life with anybody else miserable. Panayota was very formidable when she wanted to be. Kupaki is a very old-fashioned community and would have been on Panayota's side had Nitsos divorced her. He would have lost the status he had in the community."

Tsukalas, the prosecution attorney, joined in to play the devil's advocate. "Nitsos wears a black tie even today, and besides his wedding band he also wears the victim's wedding band. Is this the behavior of a man who wished his wife dead?"

"It's hypocrisy," Thanasis replied. "It makes me angry."

"Suppose that Nitsos did ask Karaiskos to kill Panayota," Palos said. "Why would Karaiskos do that?"

Thanasis answered with a question: "Who knows what Nitsos promised Karaiskos?"

The defense then brought up the rumors circulating in Kupaki about Vasilios.

"Nitsos was deliberately fueling his feud with Vasilios through the years," Thanasis explained. "He was preparing to accuse Vasilios for Panayota's murder. He was going to say that the fatal shot was actually meant for himself."

As the cross-examination continued, the attorneys began to go after each other. The defense, calling Thanasis the cornerstone of the prosecution, accused him of being commercially motivated as a witness for the prosecution. The prosecution was predictably incensed. But that only encouraged the defense, and soon their argument degenerated into a shouting match. Several minutes passed before order was finally restored, at which point Palos resumed with his questions.

"Thanasis Konandreas," he began, "is it true that you were an active member of a left-leaning organization and a vocal supporter of Communist ideology during the 40s?"

"Objection, Your Honor!" Tsukalas shouted. "This is irrelevant and immaterial to the case and is a part of the defense's tactics to discredit the witness."

"The defense is simply trying to establish the witness's political affiliations, Your Honor," Palos countered. "This is essential for the defense to demonstrate that this murder could have been an attempted political assassination that went wrong and caused the death of an innocent woman."

"Objection overruled," the Judge said. "The witness may answer the question."

"It's true that I joined the leftist organization you are referring to," Thanasis answered. "But so did Nitsos, and so did almost all the men in Kupaki at the time. We wanted to fight the Germans and the Italians, not to bring Communism into our village. I was never a Communist. These stories about me have been spread because a relative of mine was a Communist."

Palos changed directions once again. "You were a business partner of Nitsos, were you not? And is it not true that the livestock and the store you jointly own are worth a fortune?"

Thanasis laughed. "The store and the livestock are worth very little, and that's nowhere near a fortune."

"Isn't it true that Nitsos was injured fighting against the Communists in 1948?"

"For all his stories about his heroics," Thanasis answered, "Nitsos left Kupaki with his wife in 1947 when the going got rough. He returned only in 1948 when things were safer."

"Did Nitsos have any enemies?"

"None that would want to kill him."

"Yet you said earlier that in 1948 he was the band's commander for Kupaki and surrounding villages. You said that he had directed battles against the Communists."

"Lots of time has passed since those days, and by the time the murder happened, people's passions had subsided. In any case, he never fought against his fellow villagers."

"You told the court that Panayota was a formidable woman. You have told us that when she got hold of a letter Nitsos had sent his girlfriend, she went to the public square and read its contents out loud to all who cared to listen. You have also told the court that you warned her about her husband's intention to kill her. Why then did she do nothing?"

Thanasis needed only a second to mull over the question. "She didn't believe that he would go that far."

After court was adjourned later that afternoon, Thanasis stepped out into the corridor and breathed a sigh of relief. The first day was behind him. As he was complimented for his performance by some of his friends and relatives, the strapping lead attorney for the prosecution approached. Kokkinos, who stood a good head taller than Thanasis, wrapped him in a bear hug—an unprofessional but much-appreciated gesture.

"What am I to say but 'Bravo, Thanasis'? I was sitting there feeling like I was being slowly roasted over a coal fire. I could have kicked myself for not preparing you better for this sort of thing. But you're a natural. You began turning the whole show around right from the time you came clean about your criminal record. If a jury loves anything more than an honest witness with no criminal record, it's an honest witness with a criminal record who appears reformed and repentant. It gives a sense of purpose to the whole business of passing judgment."

CHAPTER 28:
WITH HONOR AND
CONSCIENCE?

THE NEXT DAY IN COURT, after the judge called everyone to order, John Gumas took the witness stand. The first to arrive at the scene of the shooting, Gumas recounted the events of the night from the moment he had found George Nitsos lifting his wife's dress to examine her injuries. He told the court how he had carried the injured woman to his yard and how, during that time, George had offered no help.

Soon after John Gumas was back in his seat, Thanasis turned to Kokkinos.

"Look at the jurors," he whispered in an urgent tone. "Look at them huddled in those three groups. There are seven over there to the left who seem to be the defense's people. There are two with their heads together to the right who don't seem to care at all. And what about the one on the front lower right, who completely avoids the others? And look at that lot in the front row. If they are law school students as they say, I am Alexander the Great. They act. They act like public relations workers for the defense. I don't like this one bit. Do you think we'll get a fair hearing?"

Thanasis was already convinced that the newspapers, particularly the *Acropolis* and the *National Herald*, were mouthpieces for the defense. A cousin of George Nitsos was the editor of one of the Athenian dailies; it was likely his opinion was influencing other journalists.

"Let's wait and see," Kokkinos replied calmly. "Here's Panaitakis now. Let's see how they treat him before we come to any hasty conclusions."

Panaitakis appeared ill at ease in his black coat and starched white

149

shirt as he took the witness stand. He fiddled with his collar as if he had earlier choked himself with a necktie, which he had clearly decided not to wear.

"What do you do for a living?" the judge asked.

"I'm a shepherd," he answered. "My family and I work for George Nitsos. We cultivate his fields and take care of his livestock as partners."

The judge pointed to George, who was seated in the front. "Is this man here the George Nitsos you work for?"

"Yes."

"Did he ever ask your help in murdering his wife?"

"Yes. He wanted me to use a hand grenade to kill Panayota. Later he wanted to frighten her horse while she was riding so it would throw her down a cliff. He also tried to push her off the branch of an oak tree another time. He also asked his cousin..."

"Objection!" Palos cried. "That is hearsay and the witness is not answering the question."

"Sustained," the Judge said. "Did Nitsos promise you anything in return?"

"He offered me the ownership of some of the land I work for him. He also said he would give me cash."

"Did you take up the job?"

"No, of course not! I may be poor, but I don't kill people for money."

"Did you ever ask Nitsos why he wanted to kill his wife?"

"At first he said it was because she couldn't give him children. Later he let on that it was because he was in love with a young woman."

"Why did you tell Konandreas about this?"

"Thanasis is Panayota's cousin. I thought he needed to know, and I thought he would be able to protect her since he was Nitsos's partner in business and was always close enough to watch him."

"Did you ask Konandreas not to confront Nitsos about this?"

"Yes."

"Why?"

"I was afraid that if Nitsos found out that I hadn't kept silent, my family would have to beg for a living. I needed the income from him. My family needed it. I was afraid of him because he was a powerful man in Kupaki."

Palos eyed Panaitakis coolly. He was going after him every bit as aggressively as he had Thanasis the day before. "Did you consider doing the crime at some later time?"

"No, definitely not."

"So did you tell Nitsos that you wouldn't do his bidding?"

"Yes."

"Really? Were you not afraid to do that in spite of all the dangers that you described earlier? Were you not afraid of the powerful man's wrath and the loss of income for your family?"

"Well," Panaitakis responded, "I didn't give him a straight answer. I didn't say no or yes. I kept delaying."

"*Delaying*? Interesting. So you were *delaying* killing Panayota. And would you have killed her if Nitsos had pressed you further?"

"Objection, Your Honor!" Kokkinos was on his feet. "This is intimidation of the witness. The defense attorney is misinterpreting the witness's words."

"Sustained. The defense may rephrase the question."

"What do you mean when you said you were delaying?" Palos asked.

"I only meant that I delayed an answer. In my mind, I was sure that I would never do anything to hurt Panayota. I tried to find a different excuse every time Nitsos brought up the subject."

"So what did you mean by saying earlier that you did not take up the offer Nitsos made you? Assuming that your story is true, you did not say no, though you did not say yes. Can you call that refusing the offer?"

"I suppose not."

"You sound less sure now. Are you sure that George Nitsos offered you land and money to kill his wife?"

"Yes, I am."

"Did Thanasis Konandreas tell you to say this at this trial?"

"Yes."

"Yes? So Konandreas asked you to say that Nitsos wanted you to kill Panayota?"

"No, he did not make me say anything."

"That was not my question. I shall rephrase it. Did Thanasis Konandreas ask you to tell the police and the court that Nitsos asked you to kill his wife Panayota?"

"Yes. He asked me to tell the truth."

"When did he do this?"

"When he visited me the morning after the murder."

"Had you spoken to anyone other than Konandreas about Nitsos's plans?" the Judge asked.

"Not at first, but when people began talking about the relationship between Nitsos and Poly, along with speaking to Thanasis Konandreas, I spoke to another cousin of Panayota and two men from a nearby village."

"Is this all true?" the judge asked. "Remember you are under oath."

"I swear by my children, and by the soul that will leave my body and will be judged one day, that every word is true. Nitsos also sent me messages from the jail. He sent them through a man from Kupaki, and offered me money if I didn't testify today."

Palos moved quickly to shift directions.

"Panaitakis, were you not a Communist? And in fact, weren't the authorities planning to send you into exile in 1947?"

"Objection, Your Honor!" Tsukalas shouted. "This is irrelevant and immaterial to the case and is a part of the defense's tactics to discredit the witness."

"That's not true," Panaitakis answered before the judge had an opportunity to rule.

Papakyriakopulos pressed on. "Panaitakis, do you recognize this handwriting?"

Panaitakis peered at the sheet of paper that the defense attorney had placed before him. "No."

"Are you sure?"

"Yes."

"Is the signature at the bottom not that of your son, Johnny?"

"It looks like his signature, but I don't recognize the handwriting."

Thanasis glanced from the witness stand to Kokkinos. What was happening?

"Objection, Your Honor," Kokkinos said, once again taking his feet. "The defense was obliged to let the prosecution know that this letter was going to be presented in court."

"Your Honor, this letter written by Johnny was brought to the defense's notice too late for its inclusion in the list of items before the court started. This letter is of vital importance to this case, and the defense wishes to enter it into evidence now."

"Objection overruled," the judge said. "The defense may proceed."

"The letter, Your Honor, was received by George Nitsos at the jail in Amfissa. In it, Johnny reveals the dastardly plot of a key witness of the prosecution, Thanasis Konandreas, to pervert the course of justice. The letter explicitly states that Konandreas has persuaded Panaitakis to give false testimony in court against Nitsos. The letter also adds that Johnny and his mother Mary are opposed to his father's greedy and Godless act. In return for this favor, this letter here says that Konandreas has promised Panaitakis Nitsos's share of the livestock that is now jointly owned by Nitsos and Konandreas. And how would Konandreas get Nitsos's share of the livestock? In the same way that Konandreas plans to secure Nitsos's share in the store and in all other assets that they jointly own as business partners: by securing a guilty verdict for Nitsos in this court!"

Palos, having brought his voice to a fever pitch, paused to milk the tension in the suddenly silent courtroom.

"That is all, Your Honor," he said, practically whispering the words. "The defense has no more questions."

The judge turned to the jury. "This court is unable to judge this case without an examination in court of additional witnesses. The conflict we just heard about the letter allegedly written by Johnny illustrates that need. And I have in addition to Johnny a list of seven more key witnesses to propose that they be summoned. The bench is asking the jury to postpone this case for those witnesses to be summoned."

Kokkinos quickly stated the prosecution's support for the proposal. Palos, not surprisingly, opposed it.

While the jury deliberated, Thanasis traded wary glances with Kokkinos. Palos had pulled a fast one. Would the jury let him get away with it?

The jury, after a brief deliberation, indicated it was ready to make a decision. "With honor and conscience," the jury foreman announced to the court, "we say ... there is no need to postpone this case."

CHAPTER 29:
PERIPLANUMENI

ONE HUNDRED AND SIXTY MILES away, I loitered outside a store in
Krokylion, the bigger village near ours in the east, about an hour by
foot from Kupaki. Dozens of locals were waiting to pick up a copy
of one of the daily newspapers. Everyone was hungry for news from
the trial, and I listened as the people in the crowd traded gossip.
Several spoke authoritatively and in detail about witnesses' answers,
pointing out the weaknesses and strengths of particular witnesses,
evaluating the performances of the attorneys, making predictions
about the outcome, and placing bets in the hopes of making some
quick money. Tonight, the second night since the trial had begun,
many of the locals were coming to the realization that George Nitsos
had substantial legal support and might just escape conviction. Many
who had pegged him guilty before the trial were suddenly adopting a
neutral stance, or even coming out in support of him.

After working my way to the front of the line, I bought a newspaper
and then started for home. I wasn't the only one. A throng of locals
were returning to Kupaki and other nearby villages, newspapers
fanned out in their hands. The ones I recognized from Kupaki, who
belonged to the defendants' faction, were carrying the *Acropolis* and
the *National Herald* while I and the others didn't have a particular
preference, carrying whatever newspaper was available at the store.

Once back at the village square in Kupaki, I watched as the locals
crowded around my new teacher, to hear him read aloud the latest
news. A few minutes later, the discussion moved from the village
square to our home, where Mitros, Thanasis's uncle, squared off
against Grandma Efthemia. The two had never gotten along, at least
not while I'd known them. For some reason, Grandma took it as a
personal slight that Mitros and his wife had never had any children.

Likewise, she disapproved of his gambling habit. He was a great card player — but never knew when to call it quits.

Though illiterate, Mitros possessed a great deal of judicial wisdom. Known in the village as the "illiterate attorney," he was always right in predicting the outcomes of cases involving land or water rights disputes, or issues over village animals' damage to crops. Now, he was predicting that the trial would end without resolution.

"*Periplanumeni*," he said. "The trial will end in *periplanumeni*."

He repeated the catchword relentlessly until finally Grandma Efthemia had endured all she could take.

"Can't you just tell us in plain Greek what that means?" she snapped.

"Well," Mitros said, clearing his throat, "it's not easy to explain it accurately to someone with no legal knowledge, but the closest meaning of *periplanumeni* in simple words is 'a case that is not won, but not lost, either.'"

"Bah!" Grandma snorted. "What on God's earth does it mean? In jail or free?"

The onus to explain fell upon Kostas, my older brother. Wanting no part of the argument, he wisely passed the burden to me. "You explain it," he said casually.

I thought a moment. "I've only heard that word in connection with the Gypsies and the Jews, Grandma," I said. "It's like saying, 'lost, moving, chased around without purpose...' You know—like being without a country or a home."

Grandma Efthemia groaned. "Can nobody speak plain Greek anymore? Gypsies and Jews indeed! What have they got to do with that *kiaratades* who killed my poor Panayota? Nobody tells me if he'll be in jail or not."

My reputation as a good student was saved a day or two later when the school teacher confessed to Efthemia that he himself had never heard the word used in relation to a court verdict.

"Mitros!" she grumbled. "He must be going soft in the head and who will look after him in his old age now?"

Mitros, when he heard about her comments, was equally dismissive. "Empty-headed old bat! And her grandson and his teacher! Empty heads, the whole lot of them!"

On the third day of the trial, Thanasis once again took a seat beside the prosecution team just before the court was called to order. He sensed something akin to normalcy—or at least a routine—settling over the courtroom. He couldn't, however, deny the other feeling nagging at him: apprehension. The defense had done a good job of muddying the waters, and the jurors, if he was any judge, appeared biased in favor of the defense.

"The prosecution wishes to make a statement, Your Honor," Kokkinos said.

"Proceed." The judge leaned back in his chair and studied the prosecution attorneys quizzically.

Tsukalas, Kokkinos's fellow prosecution attorney, took over. "We wish to register our protest against the character assassination of the prosecution witnesses Konandreas and Panaitakis by the defense without producing a shred of evidence to back their claims. First, the witnesses' political affiliations aren't relevant to this murder, which was the result of domestic problems, but the defense continues to follow a line of questioning that takes the focus away from these problems and misdirects it into the realm of politics. This is a deliberate attempt to confuse the jury. Second, even if the witnesses' politics had any bearing on this case, the defense's accusation that these witnesses are Communists is patently untrue.

"We therefore ask the court to decide if the defense is justified in following this line. If the court decides in the defense's favor, the prosecution would wish to be allowed to submit evidence that Nitsos has leftist sympathies."

"The prosecution's statement has been noted," the judge said. "The first witness of the day, Father Papazois, may be called in now."

Papazois walked confidently to the stand as if he were there to address a congregation. The stunning contrast between his white beard and the neck-to-toe black vestment and his black stove pipe hat made an immediate impression on the crowd. Here was the Greek Orthodox Church personified in all its glory and authority. Tall, with his stove pipe hat giving him four to five inches over anybody else, well built, and with a rugged handsomeness that age only seemed to enhance, Papazois smiled benevolently at the judge, the jury, the attorneys, and the crowd that stared at him.

Thanasis caught sight of Palos muttering something to his fellow defense attorney. The other attorney laughed quietly and nodded.

Kokkinos began his line of questioning by asking Papazois about public opinion in Kupaki, and Papazois told the court that, with the exception of close friends and relatives, everybody in the village thought the accused were guilty.

Kokkinos, clearly hoping to hammer the point home, read aloud from a list of names. "Please," he said, "could you tell the court how many of these people from Kupaki, to the best of your knowledge, have been solicited by George Nitsos to be present at this trial as defense witnesses?"

"All of them except one."

"The prosecution requests the court to note that twenty-five of the twenty-six people on this list who have been approached by Nitsos are not defense witnesses; only one has accepted. This shows the public's opinion of the defendants."

"Objection," Palos said. "This is hearsay. Besides, people refuse to come forward as witnesses for many reasons other than the belief that the defendants are guilty. Moreover, if all the cases in Greece were to be settled in villages like Kupaki, what is the purpose of this esteemed institution, where guilt has to be proven and not supposed?"

"Sustained," the judge said.

Tsukalas took over the examination. "What do you know of the relationship between Panayota and Nitsos?"

"It was not good," Papazois answered. "They had many problems in that marriage."

"Hearsay again," the defense attorney interjected, rising to his feet. "Where is the evidence for this?"

"Your Honor, the evidence has already been presented. The prosecution wishes to read in court that evidence, which is a letter sent to George Nitsos by his father in America. In this letter, Ioannes Nitsos, responding to news about his son's marital problems, advises him to get a divorce."

The judge allowed the letter to be read, and the prosecution's questions that followed appeared to make the defense attorneys uneasy.

When Palos finally got a chance to cross-examine the witness, he went straight to the attack. "How are you related to Thanasis Konandreas, Father?"

"He is my brother-in-law. My wife is his sister."

"And isn't it true that your brother-in-law stands to gain financially if his business partner Nitsos is out of the picture?"

"I was present along with four other men from the village when the inventory of the store was taken," Papazois answered. "The whole store was worth only around twenty thousand drachmas—certainly not more than thirty thousand drachmas. There's no big money there, contrary to the picture you present."

"Thirty thousand is quite a substantial sum for many poor people in Greece, Father. But Be that as it may, when was the inventory that you just mentioned done?"

"Soon after Nitsos was taken away by the police, suspected of his wife's murder."

"So your brother-in-law and you were making calculations about his business soon after his cousin was murdered and as soon as his business partner was away from Kupaki?"

"It was something that needed to be done. Nitsos's family had suggested it first, and in fact Zakkas, Nitsos's brother-in-law, and one of Nitsos's cousins were present and verified the inventory."

Palos tried another tack. "Was Thanasis not a Communist?"

"Are we to have political questions asked again by the defense, your honor?" Tsukalas screamed, springing to his feet.

"I would like to answer that question," Papazois snapped. "If you are talking about the baseless accusations about Thanasis being a Communist, he was cleared of those a long time ago by men of the world such as you, learned in the laws of men that you uphold. I was summoned to this city on that occasion to say what I know about Thanasis in this regard."

Thanasis listened as his story of near exile was retold by Papazois in his sonorous voice. It was true that, shortly after Thanasis's relative had been killed as a Communist, someone in the village had accused Thanasis of being a Communist sympathizer.

"I then came here to Athens," Papazois explained, "and met with authorities who were responsible for such decisions and asked for the basis of such action. There was nothing incriminating Thanasis, and the decision by the local Kupaki Nationalists force was overruled."

Palos frowned. It was clear he had hoped to chip away at Papazois's credibility—but had failed. He still, however, had one card left to play.

"The defense wishes to read aloud to the court a letter from Nitsos and Panayota," he said. "They write to Nitsos's father in America, in reply to his letter presented by the prosecution earlier."

The letter, contradicting the missive from George's father, stated that there was nothing wrong with George and Panayota's marriage and that anything he may have heard to the contrary was "mere gossip by envious people."

Before Papazois was sent away, one of the jurors asked a final question. "Upon your priesthood, Father, do you take upon yourself that with all you know, the accused are guilty and have committed the crime?"

Total silence reigned in the courtroom for a long moment.

"Yes I do," Papazois replied.

CHAPTER 30:
CORRUPT COURT

As Thanasis studied his mother-in-law, now on the witness stand, he thought she looked tired—and older than her sixty-five years. Aggeliki Gumas was straining to hear the juror's question.

"Let me repeat the question," the juror said. "Was the window of your house open or closed when the first explosion was heard?"

Aggeliki was confused. She had told the court that the window was open a couple of minutes before the shooting—when she had watched George and Panayota pass by on the path just outside her window. She had closed it moments later, however, as she had prepared for bed. Now she was being asked if it was open or closed when she'd heard the first gunshot.

The public prosecutor intervened and tried to help her understand the question, but his efforts upset two of the jurors, who complained.

"The prosecutor's intervention makes our presence superfluous, Your Honor," one juror said cuttingly. "We might as well leave this hearing if this is how it's going to be conducted."

Immediately the defense attorneys seized the opportunity to attack the public prosecutor. A long back-and-forth argument followed between the prosecution and the defense until the judge raised his gavel as a warning.

"The jurors are permitted to ask any questions freely," he said, staring sternly at everyone present.

Several minutes later, after Aggeliki had left the stand, Mary took her place. She began her testimony by describing George's plans to murder Panayota.

"I was also approached with bribes too, encouraging me not testify here," she said.

"Who was it that approached you?" Palos asked. "George Nitsos?"

"No, it was a man I know from the village where I was born. He approached me in Amfissa and promised—"

"So it was not Nitsos but someone who said he was acting on behalf of Nitsos?"

"Yes."

"And what evidence do you have that Nitsos sent him?" Palos waved off the question before she could answer it. "So let us continue with the matter at hand. When did you hear about the murder?"

"When Thanasis Konandreas told us the next morning."

"Did Thanasis Konandreas and your husband pressure you to say all this in court?"

"No," Mary answered firmly, "definitely not. And all this nonsense about my son writing a letter to Nitsos isn't true, either."

During the break, Thanasis found himself preoccupied with his suspicions that the jury was corrupt.

"I want to know how deep this goes," he told his attorneys, Kokkinos and Tsukalas.

"How deep *what* goes?" Tsukalas asked.

"Well," Thanasis answered, "I think most of the jurors favor the defense, and their vote not to let the court postpone the case and order new witnesses shows it. But there's a couple of them who act and look differently from the rest. I'm not sure if the minority can stand up to the pressure from the rest."

"Look here," Kokkinos said. "I happen to sympathize with Thanasis's doubts. The best I can offer you is this: let us test the jurors by creating a situation to see how they vote on something that benefits the prosecution. We can draw conclusions from their reaction, but I'm afraid there's not much we can do to follow up on it if we *do* think they're corrupt. I propose we hide a couple of our witnesses, claiming they got lost, and if the court asks the jury to postpone the case because they're not present, we'll know how the jury feels about us. It's a calculated risk, but it could help."

"Have you seen the other witnesses?"

Thanasis, speaking in the most frantic tone he could muster, went from one prosecution witness to the other with the same question, as soon as the court reconvened. He then moved on to the prosecution attorneys.

"Have you seen the other witnesses?" he asked Kokkinos. "This is a disaster!"

The staged disappearance of two witnesses, which the prosecution blamed on the complexities of the big city, did not impress the judge, who summoned Ntinos, the next witness in line.

Ntinos, known for his sense of humor, entered the courtroom like a popular politician marching to the front of a rally, supporters flanking him on both sides.

"Please state your age."

"I'm forty-seven years young," he informed the court.

After answering questions from the prosecution, Ntinos good-naturedly entertained defense attorney Gunaris's questions during the cross-examination.

"Yes," he said, "I've known the accused for a large part of my life. It's not easy to avoid them in that little village."

"You say it's not easy to avoid the defendants. Are you not on good terms with them then?"

"Ntinos hates no man, and no man hates Ntinos," Ntinos quipped to the delight of the audience, which burst into applause.

The judge, frowning, motioned for him to continue.

"If Panayota was shot by somebody who was trying to kill Nitsos," Ntinos then explained, "the murderer wouldn't have stopped until Nitsos was killed."

"You mentioned earlier that you've seen George Nitsos mistreating his wife," Gunaris said. "Can you tell the court how you happened to witness this?"

"It was St. George Day, shortly before the murder. I visited his home with a few friends to wish him many happy returns of the day, and we all saw him swear at Panayota and hit her—right there in front of us all. I left the house without eating any of the cake because of that." He shook his head ruefully. "And the cake did look very good."

"Speaking of beating people up," Gunaris said, "did you notice that the defendants were beaten up when they were being taken to Krokylion?"

"I noticed nothing of the sort. They looked fine and weren't complaining then."

"Isn't it true that you have some political problems with George Nitsos?"

"Not really."

"*Not really?* Can you explain your reservation?"

"Well, Nitsos used to collaborate with the Communists. In 1947 he brought them to Kupaki. He ordered all the rest of us at the village to take them food. Later, when they needed someone from the village attorneys for their statements. When I mentioned people from the village who supported the defense, their names were met with an uproar, with my brothers and I unleashing sarcasm and Uncle Mitros swearing aloud.

Grandma Efthemia, meanwhile, would react the same unforgettable way each time. First, she would ask me to reread the passage referring to the defense witness's name and views to make sure she'd heard everything correctly. But she would never wait for me to finish. She would wave at me to stop and then stand up, spread both her arms with all ten fingers aimed at the home of the person in question, and unload.

"Na, na, na, na... you..." From there, her vocabulary shrank until only epithets, physical handicaps, intellectual deformities, and cruel gossip were hurled at the defense supporter and every member of his or her family.

Once finished with her tirade, Grandma Efthemia would turn around, sit down, and ask calmly, "And then what does it say?"

CHAPTER 32:
GEORGE'S MISTRESS
TAKES THE STAND

KATINA, WHO USUALLY LOOKED STYLISH, worldly, and a bit older than her nineteen years, appeared young and vulnerable on the witness stand, Thanasis thought. She answered the defense attorney's questions with a mixture of naiveté and a shrewd artfulness beyond her years.

Her father was a farmer, she said. Of his five children, she was the only one with a high school education and the ambition to leave her village for a better life. In February of 1953, she had transferred to another high school. In need of a local guardian, she had sought and received the supervision of George Nitsos, whom her family knew. She had wanted to get her high school diploma first and then immigrate to Canada, but she had been afraid she would never graduate.

"Why did you think you would never graduate?" she was asked.

"Because George Nitsos was on good terms with my teachers, and he would have tried to keep me where I was."

"When did you realize that this was the case?"

"I knew right from the start that he was attracted to me," Katina said, adding, "Of course, I didn't let him have sex with me at first."

"So did you give in when he forced you to later?"

"No, I didn't have sex with him at first because I didn't want him to think that I would sleep with anyone. Later, I let him because I wanted his protection."

"Was Nitsos the first man you had sex with?" A defense attorney asked.

There he goes, Thanasis thought, *and he knows the answer, too.* The defense was going to try to portray George as a good family man led astray by a loose woman.

"No," Katina answered. "I had had sex with a man two years before that."

"Were you still having a relationship with that man at the same time as your relationship with Nitsos?"

"No, I'm not that sort of a girl. That man was married, and I didn't want to continue and cause problems in his marriage."

"Did you want to cause problems in Nitsos's marriage, then?"

"Well, he was not going to leave his wife. He was not in love with me, and I was not in love with him."

"Were you not afraid of other consequences?"

"I was afraid of becoming pregnant, but he told me that he was being careful about that. Anyway, it was only five or six times until I finished high school in June."

"Did Nitsos give you any gifts in return?"

"He bought me a watch for my name day."

"Did your family not suspect anything?"

"My father thought of him as a respectable person to have as a local guardian. We never did anything suspicious at my place. It was always elsewhere in the village during the summer."

"Did Nitsos ever ask you to sleep with other men?"

"No, he never did. And I wouldn't have if he did."

"Did he ever try to end the relationship?"

"No, but I knew that he wouldn't have a hard time if it ended."

"Did you ever try to end it?"

"No, but each time we had sex, I would tell him about my plans for the future, and he would say that I needed to finish school first and then become a teacher."

"Did you know that he had relationships with other women?"

"No, I didn't."

"Did he ever ask you to marry him?"

"No."

"Did you ever ask him to marry you?"

"No. We both knew that this was nothing to do with love and marriage. He always said he would find a good husband for me."

"Did he offer to pay you fifty gold sovereigns as a dowry when he did find you a good husband?"

"I don't know how that rumor got around. I don't remember him saying anything like that."

"Did he ever pay you for your services?"

"Of course not!" Katina shot back, her eyes flaming. "I'm not that sort of a girl."

"So you got no money from him, then?"

"Well, when he came to Lidoriki, he would leave forty or fifty drachmas with me, but that wasn't payment for services or anything dirty like you're trying to make it sound."

"Did Nitsos ever talk to you about his wife?"

"Yes. He used to say that she was smart and a good housewife. He was proud that she would never accept any unkind things that people told her about him."

"Is it true that in May 1953 you had an opportunity to go to America to work?"

"Yes."

"Why did you not take it up?"

"George was against it. He said that it was better to become a teacher here than a cleaning woman in America. He took the papers from the postman, and when I asked him about it, he only said that they were from the consulate; he didn't give them to me."

"Even though these papers came in an envelope addressed to you?"

"That's right."

"Did you not ask him to give them to you?"

"No, I didn't. I had to re-sit an examination in September and was too busy preparing for that to bother about the papers at that time."

Thanasis glanced from Katina to a throng of journalists seated off to the side, all of them furiously scribbling in their notebooks. Like the rest of the onlookers in the crowded courtroom, they were buzzing with excitement at this latest revelation. What would George's mistress say next?

"Did you meet Nitsos on the day of the murder?"

"It was a Sunday, and he had been to church in the morning. I saw him sitting outside the church and went up to him and spoke to him."

"What did you talk about?"

"Nothing much. I think we said hello to each other, but he seemed to want to be alone. I thought he was preoccupied again with the repairs of the church building and didn't stay around much longer to bother him."

"Was this the last time you both met?"

"No, he came back to the church later on, in the evening. He was there to ring the bell for the people working on the road to Krokylion."

"Was he better disposed to speak to you this time?"

"Yes."

"Did you stay outside the church to speak?"

"Yes."

"What did you do there?"

"Well, he pulled me to him, and we stood like that for some time. There was no time for all that, because he wanted it all done in a hurry."

"What did he want done in a hurry?"

"I can't say that here in front of all these people. He... you know..." Katina's voice dropped to a nearly inaudible level. "He wanted... satisfaction."

"Do you mean sexual gratification?"

"Yes," she stuttered.

"Did he threaten you with dire consequences if you let the secret out?"

"He didn't threaten me. He only said that I shouldn't talk about this." She appeared to suppress an involuntary shudder. "Even if someone asked me with a knife to my throat or removed all the teeth in my mouth."

"Are you sure he was not referring to the murder of Panayota that he was planning?"

"No, he never planned with me to murder his wife. He was talking about situations like my father finding out."

"Why do you think he was talking about knives and removing teeth suddenly then?"

"It was because his wife had heard about us. He told me that someone—I think it was Effie—told her godmother Marula, and she told his wife. This was when he said that his wife had stood by him and didn't accept what others told her about him. He wanted me to be like that, too."

"Where were you when the murder took place?"

"I was at home."

"Did you hear the shots?"

"No."

"When did you hear that Panayota was murdered?"

"When someone woke me up and told me that the Nitsoses had been murdered. At first, everyone was saying that both he and his wife had been murdered. On the morning after the murder, Konandreas told me that they had arrested Nitsos as a suspect. He said, 'That beast has killed the woman.' He told me that the rumor in the village was that Nitsos had said many things to the police about me and that I should plan what to say. He suggested that I accuse Nitsos in revenge for all that he had done to me."

Thanasis frowned. Katina was making it sound like he had encouraged her to frame George.

"What advice did Nitsos have for you?" the prosecution attorney asked, no doubt hoping to minimize the damage. "Did you not try to meet him after he was accused and put under police custody?"

"I did go to his house. When I tried to enter, the policeman on guard there did not let me. So I went to my sister's house next door. At noon, a policeman came and took me to the captain, who took my statement."

"I was coming to that statement. There are many discrepancies between that statement and what you have said here, and many contradictions even within that statement. Can you explain these?"

"I lied at first about my relationship with George, but when they told me everything he had told them, I felt there was no point in hiding things."

"So Nitsos told you not to say anything about your relationship, while he himself spoke about it as soon as he was arrested?"

"They must have made him. I tried to keep my word to him. I didn't say anything about us at first."

"But you still must have lied if what you're saying now is true. For example, you told the police captain that Nitsos must have murdered his wife to marry Poly, but you told this court today that you didn't know of any other relationships Nitsos had with women. How do you explain this?"

"It's possible that I told the captain that he organized the murder for Poly and not for me. What I meant was that, if he did commit the murder, it must have been for her, because I knew it certainly wasn't for me. That wasn't the kind of relationship we had.

"The captain threatened me," she continued. "So I said some of the things out of fear. Later he also told me that nothing would happen to me if I said whatever I wanted to, so I said some things because I felt revengeful toward Nitsos for saying all those things about me. I have no honor left in the whole village. People look at me like dirt!"

"So you didn't tell the captain that Nitsos killed his wife?"

"No, I didn't say that even when I was feeling revengeful. I don't believe that he killed his wife. Anyway, I don't know if the captain of the county police told the captain from Krokylion to write down different things than what I told him."

"Surely, you know what the statement taken down contained," Tsukalas insisted, "because your signature is on it!"

"The captain read my statement back to me before I signed it, but I didn't read it myself before I signed it. It may have been different from what I said."

"Is it true that Nitsos's sister read you a letter sent by him from jail, begging you to be patient and promising to marry you when he comes out?"

"No, I don't remember any such letter."

"Is it true that you told your cousin Zanias that Nitsos had committed the murder?"

"No, that's a lie. He's saying that because he has indecent designs on me, and I've discouraged him. He told me to accuse George Nitsos. He said it would be better for me if they hanged Nitsos. He visited my house four or five days after the murder and asked me to go away from the village for a day with him, but I refused. Then he beat me up."

"Why didn't you say anything about this earlier?"

"I did. I took him to court. When my relatives pressured me, I had to withdraw the suit."

CHAPTER 33:
FIRST-HAND NEWS

ZANIAS, KATINA'S COUSIN, TOOK HIS place at the witness stand. His tall stature and upright posture, Thanasis thought, contrasted sharply with the image Katina had portrayed of him during her testimony.

"How did you find out about your cousin's relationship with Nitsos?" the prosecution asked.

"She confided to me that Nitsos was her lover, and that he was supporting her high school education."

"Did she tell you that Nitsos was going to marry her?"

"No."

"Did she tell you that Nitsos was planning to murder his wife?"

"No, but after the murder, she told me that she had given a statement against Nitsos. She also told me that she would retract it because she was in love with him."

"Do you know why she had this change of heart after giving the police the statement against her lover?"

"She told me that one of Nitsos's sisters had read out a letter to her that Nitsos had sent, asking her to retract what she had said against him and promising to marry her when he comes out of jail within three years."

"How did you react to that?"

"I asked her if she was going to marry a murderer, and she replied that Nitsos didn't pull the trigger himself. I think, however, that deep inside Katina believes that Nitsos had asked Karaiskos to kill his wife. She also told me not to be concerned about her since Nitsos's family would support her. In my opinion, Katina knows more than she lets on."

"How was your relationship with Nitsos?"

"He has always been friendly with me, possibly because he wanted me to look the other way when it came to his relationship with Katina."

"Were you not suspected of murdering Panayota at one point?"

"Yes, this was Thanasis Konandreas's misunderstanding, because he thought I could have done it in revenge for Nitsos's relationship with Katina."

"Do you own a gun?"

"Yes."

"What kind?"

"A twelve gauge."

"Similar to the one used for the murder, then?"

"Yes," Zanias stuttered.

"Was your gun checked by the police after the murder?"

"No."

The next witness, fifty-year-old Demos, explained that in 1946 his sister visited him and told him that Nitsos had sent her to ask if he was willing to kill Panayota for forty gold sovereigns.

"And what was your response?"

"I felt insulted. I cursed her and sent her away."

"Why did you not report this?"

"I intended to go to the police, but when I realized that the police force in Krokylion had been disbanded because of the civil war, I thought the next best thing would be to tell Thanasis Konandreas."

"Why Konandreas and not one of the victim's other relatives?"

"Of all the male relatives she had, he was the closest to her."

"Did Nitsos ever ask you this directly?"

"No."

"Did he have the chance to, had he wanted to?"

"Yes. I did see a lot of him after that. We fought together during the civil war from 1948-to-1950 as commanders of our village militias. Nitsos never mentioned this to me."

George Nitsos, much to Thanasis's consternation but no doubt to the delight of the defense, stood up suddenly to defend himself. "Tell me, Demos," he said authoritatively, "between 1947 and 1950, when we were fighting the Communists, when there was so much chaos and we were peppering the village with land mines, could I not have placed a mine in my wife's usual path without having any suspicion directed at me?"

"Yes," Demos answered. "I suppose you could have."

———————∞———————

Polyxeni returned the next day to our village and my siblings and I were surprised with several school supplies, including a handful of ballpoint pens, which we'd never seen before. We were so excited to experiment with our new pens that we hardly noticed Uncle Mitros and Grandma Efthemia behaving amicably as Mother gave them first-hand news of the trial.

"Thanasis and his attorneys don't think that Nitsos and Karaiskos will be out free," she said, "but they think the court may find the case *peplanimeni*."

At the sound of the word, Mitros and Efthemia exchanged glances.

"What did I say!" Mitros cried, nearly jumping for joy. "What did I say! And all these empty heads here thought I was mad."

Grandma Efthemia could only snort in derision.

"That's exactly what I've been telling them all along, Polyxeni dear," Mitros continued. "And they all drove me crazy, including that moron of a teacher."

"*Papu*," I said, joining the conversation, "you were saying *periplanumeni*, not *peplanimeni*."

"Ha!" an overjoyed Efthemia shot back. "This is what comes of bandying about big words without even learning to read and write."

"What difference does it make if they both mean the same thing?" Mitros said defensively.

Mother tactfully changed the topic, offering them *ouzo* and feta cheese. She then went on to describe the trial and how the defense had prevented any further witnesses from appearing for the prosecution.

"The jury agreed with them," she said. "One of the jurors came forward and announced, 'With honor and conscience, we have decided that there's no need to postpone the case by bringing in additional witnesses,' and the prosecution attorneys began to—"

"Honor and conscience, eh, Polyxeni?" Mitros said, interrupting. "What a joke!"

CHAPTER 34:
THE LIST

PAGONIS, THE SHEPHERD OF NITSOS, was called to the witness stand next. He said that he went to his hut and slept after he borrowed the flashlight from Panayota, but Karaiskos called him sometime after midnight from the top of a hill next to his hut and asked him to keep him company. Because Karaiskos was there, he claimed it would have been impossible to go to the village to shoot Panayota and come back. He added that Karaiskos's gun was very old and worn out, and too unreliable to be used to kill someone.

"Have you ever seen your employer, George Nitsos, mistreating his wife?" the defense asked.

"No. She was a good woman, and he actually treated her as one."

"So you have never come across any abuse of her by him?"

"No, I told you just now. He even treated her with more respect than many men give their wives. He gave her more freedom."

"What sort of freedom?"

"Well, she would often join him to play cards at the village store. You won't find many men in Kupaki allowing their wives to do that."

"Were you yourself arrested after the murder?" Kokkinos, from the prosecution, asked.

"Yes, and they kept me in the school and then let me go."

"Is it normal for Karaiskos to call you from the hills as you say he did on the night of the murder?"

"Yes."

"Was he letting you know he was there, or did he really want your company?"

"Are you saying that he did that to show that he was not in Kupaki to do the murder? I don't think so."

"Please answer the question."

"No, he really wanted my company."

"You've been questioned... let me see." Kokkinos rummaged through his notes. "Four times in total so far. Is that correct?"

"Yes."

"Why then did you make a statement about this shouted conversation with Karaiskos across the hills several months after the murder? Why didn't you give this important information earlier?"

"No one asked me about it."

"You said earlier that Karaiskos's gun was useless. Can you explain how he was able to kill a partridge with that gun on the morning of September 6, 1953, the same day the murder took place?"

"I don't know," Pagonis said with a shrug.

"You said in your initial statement that it would have been impossible for the killer to miss Nitsos, because he was holding a flashlight. You later retracted this. Can you explain why?"

"I gave the initial statement in the village to the police. They didn't read back that part to me before I signed it. They could have just put anything in that statement and not read that bit to me. Because I can't read, I wouldn't have known the difference."

The judge then turned to the jury and once again asked them to postpone the case in order to summon new witnesses, but the jury again denied his request.

Thanasis, still seated by the prosecution, could only shake his head in disbelief. It was obvious the jury was biased. Why couldn't anyone else see it?

"Yes, I know what I'm saying," said Pantoulias, a defense witness. "I heard Konandreas on the telephone on the day after the murder. He was seeking help from many villagers to spread the rumor that it was Nitsos who murdered Panayota."

Pantoulias was equally certain about the shell from Socrates's gun. "Yes, I do know about guns—that's why the county police captain asked for my help with the test-firing he organized. He asked Karaiskos to fire his shotgun into the ground from six meters away. He then compared the shell from the crime scene with the shell from the recent shot and said that the two didn't match."

"Are you sure about this?" the defense attorney asked.

"Very sure. The only suspicious thing about Karaiskos's gun was that it smelled of powder even before the test firing—as though it had been fired not long before."

The judge interrupted Pantoulias to ask a question of his own. "If you found out such a crucial piece of information as the shell found at the crime scene being different from the shell from the test firing," he said, "why then did you not offer yourself as a defense witness at that stage?"

"I didn't want to waste my time like this in courts. I thought that the information would be conveyed to the right authorities anyway. It was only recently that I came to know that innocent people might be punished because of a mix-up with the shells. I haven't been subpoenaed. I came of my own volition."

When it came time for the cross-examination, Kokkinos wasted no time attacking Pantoulias's claim that the captain had sent the wrong shells to the forensic experts. "Are you aware that the captain was on good terms with Nitsos, who was a lieutenant under him?"

"Yes."

"Why would the captain try to incriminate Nitsos, rather than favor him?"

"I don't know."

"The captain had several policemen with him. Why did he ask your help when you weren't even known to him?"

"I don't know."

Miltiades, George's brother-in-law and the next defense witness, took the stand. "Was Nitsos's decision to stay for dinner on the night of the murder a last-minute one?" the defense asked.

"On the contrary," Miltiadis answered, "the women in my house had planned this much earlier. I understand the implication by the prosecution that this was prompted by Nitsos in order to kill his wife, but nothing could be further from the truth. After dinner, we partied and played cards until about eleven that night. And it was Panayota who decided the time they left. At the end of a round, she said, 'Let's leave, George,' and though George wanted to stay and play another round, he gave in to Panayota's insistence."

"How soon after they left did you hear the shots?"

"Shortly afterward."

"And did you go to help?"

"Yes. I helped my brother-in-law transfer his wife to the Gumases' yard. George helped dress Panayota's wounds and was asking for a doctor and the police before he fainted from grief."

"Did you hear Panayota say, 'Now that you have devoured me...' to your wife, Alexandra?"

"No, I definitely did not."

"Did you hear Konandreas tell the victim, 'Vasilios did not kill you; I told you who would,' at all?"

"No, but I heard him offer to go to the doctor, which he never did."

"Do you know of any problems in the Nitsoses' marriage?"

"George loved his wife and married her willingly, contrary to the gossip of some people in Kupaki. George never told me about any marital problems, nor did Panayota complain about him."

"So Nitsos never talked about killing his wife?"

"Most definitely not," Zakkas answered indignantly. "George could have got rid of Panayota peacefully through a divorce. If he was as fraudulent as the prosecution has been claiming, why could he not have used that fraud to find a couple of witnesses to testify against Panayota and thus get a divorce? He could easily have done that and moved to America!"

"Panayota had eight cousins. Do you know if any of them except Thanasis Konandreas has sought to take Nitsos to court?"

"No. And that proves that Konandreas is motivated by selfish interests, and not by love for a cousin, which the other seven cousins surely also feel."

During the cross-examination, the prosecution picked up on what Zakkas had said about Vasilios. "Why didn't you do anything at the time, if you suspected Vasilios? You saw him at the Gumas residence."

"What could I have done? Arrest him? Attack him? I'm not the kind of person to get into physical confrontations, and it's my understanding that good citizens shouldn't take the law into their own hands. Besides, I didn't want to have anything to do with Vasilios. That man's presence made me feel that night as though rattlesnakes were crawling all over my body."

"Are you privy to any previous animosity between Nitsos and Konandreas?"

"No. If they had any differences, they weren't apparent, because they treated each other civilly enough, as business partners do."

"So there were no jealousies or other ill feelings between the two, as far as you know?"

"As far as I know, George had no reason to be jealous of Konandreas. He was above Konandreas in social status and financially. I can't say the same for Konandreas. He may well have been secretly jealous of George. He was always second to George—vice president of the church council, of which George was president, for example. Konandreas is a Communist and so probably against George's Nationalistic beliefs and work."

"Are you aware that Nitsos, a married man, was having an affair with a high school student, Katina?"

"I don't approve of such things, but I don't believe that having an extramarital relationship makes a man a murderer."

"Nitsos has fooled him," Thanasis muttered to a prosecution attorney sitting beside him. "It's so sad that he's taken his support for Nitsos to levels beyond logic and comprehension."

After Miltiades's testimony, the court broke for several days, with the break coinciding with several holidays. Afterward, when it was scheduled to reconvene, Demosthenes Dapontes, the lone juror Thanasis had pegged as impartial, asked to be excused due to illness. With no alternate juror to take his place, the court had no choice but to accept his request and prolong the recess. The public prosecutor, then asked for and received permission to summon several expert witnesses, including forensic specialists.

Thanasis, meanwhile, met one night with his attorneys to discuss his biggest fear: a rigged jury.

"They have twice," he began, "refused the judge's request to postpone the case. What does that mean to you? And they act and ask questions like defense attorneys. Do you need more?"

"We must be patient," Tsukalas counseled, "and focus on the positive."

"What about the juror who claimed illness?" Thanasis countered. "By doing so, he gave the court the time to seek more witnesses. What does he know? What does the court know?"

Kokkinos and Tsukalas traded wary glances. Thanasis's concerns were impossible to ignore. So, too, was the political climate around them. In post-war Greece, you could never be sure of a fair deal— unless you knew the right people.

The three men set to work preparing a list with the names of all the jurors. Then they began to study several variables for each juror: the village or town he hailed from, his family and clan loyalties, his workplace, his current neighborhood, and his political affiliation. Could they encourage any of them to reconsider their verdict? If all else failed, Thanasis and his attorneys agreed, there was always plain old money, whose color often changed the tint of people's perceptions.

Kokkinos and Tsukalas highlighted the names of two jurors on the list. Of everyone in the jury, the two men seemed to be keeping their distance from the majority.

"You've got to pull any strings you can to make sure these two jurors' minds aren't swayed by the defense," Kokkinos said.

Thanasis frowned. "I don't have any connections in the big city except with a few *galatades* who moved here ages ago," Thanasis said, referring to the old milkmen who had decades earlier relocated from the country to Athens. "Those strings are too long to even try pulling."

"You never know," Kokkinos said. "The *galatades* and their children aren't selling milk and yogurt anymore. Most of them are very well educated, and many have important and influential positions now. Some long strings can be pretty strong. They pull a lot of weight from very far away."

Thanasis left the meeting with a heavy heart. The city's neon lights were not enough to lift his dark mood.

That night at the Gumas house, Thanasis sat down with his brothers-in-law to cull through their memories. Soon they were bringing up names they'd long forgotten and analyzing each man's political power, social standing in the community, and willingness to take the risk that went along with attempting to influence the decision of a court of law.

Soon they came up with a list of four people that might be able to help them. There was Apostolos, Thanasis's cousin who was an attorney; Vuleftes, the powerful attorney and politician; Giatros, a medical doctor and rich socialite; and Eftaxias, a parliamentarian and National Undersecretary of Economy.

The challenge before Thanasis now was to persuade the men on that list to wield their influence in the service of a just cause.

CHAPTER 35:
INFLUENCE

THE FIRST MAN ON THANASIS's list was his cousin, Apostolos. A cosmopolitan attorney with rustic roots, he was at first hesitant to believe that the jury could be so corrupt. But after Thanasis's presentation, he worriedly studied the list of jurors' names.

"I'm afraid I don't know any of these men," Apostolos said. "Who else are you going to see?"

"I plan to see Giatros, Eftaxias, and Vuleftes."

"Eftaxias is a good one," Apostolos said, still studying the list. "It appears these jurors are all bank employees, and their bank belongs administratively to his ministry of national economy. His father was a director of the Bank of Greece."

A few minutes later, Thanasis was approaching the ministry of finance. As he neared the building, he couldn't help wryly noting that, with the municipal elections for the new mayor of Athens in the offing, this was just the right moment to approach politicians for favors.

After looking him up and down, the man at the front desk quickly dashed Thanasis's hopes of a meeting. "Eftaxias is mourning his mother, who has just passed away," the man said. "Besides, the minister will be busy with several important appointments in Greece and abroad as soon as he's able to return to work."

In other words, Thanasis thought, *Don't bother coming back.*

Thanasis continued on toward the city center, arriving at Vuleftes's office before noon. By the time Thanasis had finished greeting the many familiar faces he knew there, Vuleftes appeared.

"Thanasis," he murmured, "how come you're here instead of at the court?"

"May I have a word with you in private?" Thanasis asked.

"What's there to talk about, Konandreas?" the attorney and politician asked, suddenly switching to Thanasis's surname. "You've made an embarrassment of the village, and your trial has resulted in smearing the reputation of unmarried Kupaki girls."

Thanasis was so taken aback by Vuleftes's comment that he could only gasp in shock. "I'm not here to talk about those girls who are still alive," he finally responded with all the dignity he could muster. "I want to talk to you about a dead woman. She was called Panayota."

Vuleftes merely raised his eyebrows.

"The girls you're talking about have built their own reputations," Thanasis continued, his anger building. "I have no responsibility for their fate."

Several attorneys who knew Thanasis drew closer.

"I'm staying out of this business," Vuleftes declared with a wave of the hand. "I'm not talking to you. I'm not talking to the other side. If you've decided to take each other's eyes out, do so by all means, but do leave me out of it."

"If that's the way you feel, then so be it," Thanasis shot back, "but do you remember how many times you've said right here in your office that they're the murderers?"

Vuleftes, the great attorney, politician, and ex-parliamentarian, visibly reddened. "If this is all you want to talk about, we're finished! No more discussion! Not one word!"

"Right!" Thanasis snapped. "Let them out, then, free to have fun as usual, and come and see and enjoy them with pride, dancing at the village square—the ones you once called murderers!"

"Out!" a livid Vuleftes shouted. "Out!"

Thanasis, one step ahead of him, was already bounding down the marble steps to the sidewalk. For once the noisy hawking of street peddlers selling pretzels, pistachio nuts, and lottery tickets sounded soothing to his ears.

Disregarding Thanasis's advice, Papazois, who was also in Athens, decided to try his own luck at speaking with Vuleftes, but before Papazois could even make his case, the attorney cut him off.

"I know why you're here," he said.

"Listen, Vuleftes," Papazois said calmly, "you know Nitsos did it. You have told me so right here in your office."

"To give one's opinion is one thing," Vuleftes replied, "to actively take sides is another."

"I know, Vuleftes. I know your cousin is married to Nitsos's brother, and a relationship like that is not to be trifled with, but for the soul of Panayota, I implore you to help."

The attorney fell silent. Was he reconsidering his position?

Papazois decided to press on. "Vuleftes, as a priest, I know about forgiveness. Forgiveness is the balm for the soul that repents, not the right of every sinner. Tell me, is there anything anybody can ever do to make Nitsos repent? Don't you see what he's doing in court, accusing everybody from our village of things they've never even dreamt of doing?"

"I'm totally disgusted by the shame the trial has brought Kupaki," Vuleftes said, "and I want to stay out of this fight."

"Vuleftes, Nitsos will return to the village more arrogant than ever before because he's now a celebrity—and a free one at that. And that will drive Thanasis to the edge. There's no saying how much worse that could make things for our village. Just think: punishment for Nitsos would not only be just; but also it would protect our community."

The priest felt his voice falter as he spoke. It was clear he was fighting a losing battle. Vuleftes had already made up his mind and would not be moved. He continued on in the hopes of winning the man over, but eventually he found himself trudging out in defeat, his humble exit not unlike Thanasis's before him.

Later that evening, Thanasis and Papazois made their way in the cool November air toward Giatros's residence. Giatros was not a politician; he was a humanist who deeply felt Panayota's loss.

"Is there anything we can do?" he asked.

Thanasis shared in detail his experience with Apostolos and Eftaxias, and their failure to persuade the doctor's cousin, Vuleftes.

"Do you believe that all ten jurors have already made up their minds?" Giatros finally asked.

"Some of the jurors don't appear influenced yet," Thanasis replied, "which is why we're trying so hard to find someone who might be able to prevent the defense from influencing them."

"Do you know their names, their jobs, their places of birth, and so on?" Sofia, Giatros's wife, asked.

"Yes", Thanasis answered. He removed the list he was working on from his pocket and handed it to the couple.

Sofia and Giatros studied it carefully, pausing to whisper to each other on occasion as if in church. As they traded whispers, their faces grew more optimistic. Soon the suspense was more than Thanasis could take.

"We couldn't help noticing that one of the men works at the Farmers Bank of Greece," Giatros finally said. "Sofia's brother is the bank director. He might be able to help with this particular juror."

CHAPTER 36:
EXPERTS

THE STATE POLICE MAJOR STOOD upright in the witness stand and spoke with authority. "I arrived at Kupaki on the afternoon of Monday, September 7, 1953," he said. "I made a thorough inspection of the crime scene. It didn't take me long to establish that two people could not walk side by side on that path, contrary to what George Nitsos claims. We tried to do this in the daytime and found it impossible, so there is no way this could have been done at night when the visibility was low. There is a fourteen-foot drop into the ravine. The way the Nitsoses were hit by the shots also contradicts Nitsos's claim that he and his wife were walking side by side when the shots were fired."

"Did you also examine the guns owned by the people in the area?" the prosecution asked.

"Yes," the major answered. "I found that only one of the guns smelled of powder, as it had been fired not long ago. This was the shotgun of Socrates Karaiskos. Karaiskos said that he had fired the gun to kill a partridge the day before."

"Did you have any means other than the smell of gunpowder to establish that the shot was fired from Karaiskos's gun?"

"The shell from the crime scene matched the shell from the test firing done with Karaiskos's gun. More specifically, the marks made by the firing pin were exactly the same, and this is highly unlikely to be a coincidence."

"Could anyone have placed the shell at the crime scene to incriminate Karaiskos?"

"Had the crime scene been left unguarded after the murder, this could have happened, but this wasn't the case. Also, only someone who knew where to find a shell from Karaiskos's gun could have planted the evidence."

"Are you aware that there are complaints that the shell was not checked for fingerprints?"

"I am. I'm also aware that checking for fingerprints is standard procedure and it would have been done as a matter of course. If it wasn't, it would have been a serious omission on the part of an officer of the law."

"Would it not have been easier for Karaiskos, if he is indeed the culprit, to clean his gun of the smell of powder than to show the investigators a dead partridge and say that he had fired the gun recently to kill that bird?"

"It would have been easier, definitely, but perhaps he didn't know that his gun would be examined closely, or perhaps he wasn't thinking straight."

"Why would the perpetrator of such a well-planned murder, with the assistance of an accomplice, not remove the shell after the shots were fired?"

"It was dark," the major said. "Perhaps he couldn't find the shell. Perhaps he didn't think about removing it from the spot. All these things depend on how much presence of mind the perpetrator had. A well-planned murder is not necessarily a well-executed one."

"Could the captain of the county police have substituted the shell at the murder scene with the shell from Karaiskos's gun?"

"Highly unlikely. He is too conscientious to have done it by design, and too professional to have done it by mistake."

"Does that description fit an officer who slept in the house of a suspect?"

"It is true Vasilios was a suspect and that the captain slept in his house. Often the police do this to know more about a suspect."

Three forensic experts for the prosecution and one hired by the defense took the stand next.

The experts argued a lot, but by the end of the day, they had all agreed on two things: the shell had come from Socrates's gun, and it would have been impossible for the killer to miss George and hit Panayota if the intended target had indeed been George himself.

Eleni, George's forty-seven-year-old sister, was one of his most vocal defenders.

"Was Panayota invited to dinner at the Zakkases that night?"

"Yes, I was one of the people who invited her. She had left the Zakkases and gone home, but when Nitsos arrived there later, we had this idea of all the family eating together. This was not pre-planned, and George had nothing to do with it. Alexandra and I were the ones who convinced him to stay. He did say that Panayota would be waiting at home for him, but we told him that we would ask her to come over."

"When did the Nitsoses leave after dinner?"

"At about eleven. It was Panayota who decided to leave at that time. George wanted to stay, but he could never say no to his wife, so he decided to go. It is all nonsense, all this talk that's going on now about George planning the whole thing and having someone waiting to kill his wife at a particular time."

"Did you hear Panayota say, 'Now that you have devoured me'?"

"I was with her the whole time after she was carried to the Gumases' yard," Eleni answered. "I didn't hear her say anything like that. She was in pain, screaming and moaning. She couldn't have said anything so coherent."

Thirty-eight-year-old Eudokia, who took the witness stand after Eleni, confirmed that she was George's first cousin and lived next door to the Nitsoses.

"You get to know a lot about your neighbors in a small village like Kupaki," she said. "I never heard George and Panayota arguing. And it's all nonsense what people are now saying about Panayota not sleeping at home and finding places in the village to escape from George's abuse. I would have known if something like that had happened."

"Are you aware that George Nitsos has himself admitted in a statement that he tore Panayota's dress during a fight on a holiday?" the prosecution attorney questioned her.

"No," Eudokia stuttered. "I didn't know that."

George Nitsos, seated beside his team of attorneys, couldn't remain silent any longer.

"Your Honor," he said, addressing the judge directly, "I want to clarify this. The prosecution is as usual twisting my words to suit their purposes. On that holiday, we had visitors in Kupaki, and I went home to ask my wife if she would like to go out into the countryside where the livestock were, but my wife wanted to come the way she was dressed at home, so I grabbed her arm affectionately to pull her into the house to where her clothes were. The old dress she was wearing at home ripped. This was completely unintentional."

The judge studied Nitsos quizzically. "So you affectionately ripped your wife's dress?"

The courtroom exploded in laughter, and the judge, no doubt secretly pleased by the response to his humor, called for order.

CHAPTER 37:
VENDETTA

Thanasis noticed several people around him sit up in their seats expectantly when Socrates Karaiskos himself walked to the witness stand.

"How well do you know George Nitsos?"

"I know him very well. He is my *koumbaros*—my best man—and he and his wife are... *were*... the godparents of my child. My family and his had a very good relationship."

"Where were you when the murder happened at about eleven p.m. on Sunday, September 6, 1953?"

"Two days before, starting on Friday, I was among the men working on the road to Krokylion. I had arranged with my wife that I would be back on Monday to dig up the potatoes. On the Sunday morning you asked me about, I was out hunting."

"Did you get anything?"

"Yes, I shot and killed a partridge. I had it with me with its feathers still not plucked when I visited my father-in-law, who lives near the spot where I did the hunting. We had lunch together."

"What did you do after lunch?"

"I took a nap, and then I returned to my hut, and then I took my lambs out to graze. Later, I went to Pagonis's hut, where I stayed until about an hour after sunset."

"What did you do after that?"

"I went to my hut and fed my lambs some clover. About an hour after that, between eleven p.m. and midnight, I was on the top of a hill. I made a fire there around midnight and went to sleep."

"Did anyone else see you there?"

"Only my dogs. I didn't know then that I would have to come to this court and give an account of all that I did on that day."

"When did you find out about the murder?"

"When my wife came to see me early Monday morning, she began crying, and I knew something was wrong. When I calmed her down and asked her what the matter was, she told me that the Nitsoses were shot, that Panayota was dead and George was injured but alive."

"Did you not ask your wife who had done this?"

"I did. And she said that she heard at the village that it was Vasilios. I left for Kupaki at once."

"But not before hiding your gun. Why did you do that?"

"When I reached the outskirts of the village, I met Johnny, Panaitakis's son. He told me that there were policemen at the village and they were examining people's guns. I was worried that I might get into trouble for not having a proper permit. I told Johnny that, and he advised me to hide my gun somewhere before entering the village. So I buried it under a cedar."

"Did you meet Nitsos?"

"I went straight to his house to offer him my condolences."

"When were you asked to bring the gun you had hidden?"

"When I got to George's, the local police chief was there and he was ordering his men to collect all the guns in the village. He asked me for mine, and I went and got it."

"Were you arrested after the gun was test fired?"

"Not right away. The captain asked me if I had fired my gun. I told him that I had killed a partridge on Sunday morning and that I still hadn't plucked its feathers. He told me not to pluck the feathers until he gave me permission to. So I left it as it was. On Monday afternoon, Konandreas asked me to go dig a grave for Panayota. Later, I went to the school where my wife was giving a statement and returned home with her. I had to come back to the school again, because when the captain of the county police arrived, he wanted my statement, too. He was the one who arrested me. He then went with Katina to sleep in Vasilios's house."

"Had you already given your statement when you were arrested?"

"No, the captain took my statement on Tuesday morning around eleven a.m. and then whipped me, asking me to give a false confession that I was the one who committed the murder. They interrogated me in the Kupaki School without even giving me water to drink. They threatened me and kept whipping me. In the end, they asked me to sign a statement they had prepared that was not even read to me."

"Did you then go to Krokylion?"

"Yes, they took me to Krokylion and put me in a dark cellar and whipped me again. They kept whipping me all the way to jail."

"How was your relationship with Nitsos and Panayota?"

"They were a good couple, and they helped me. Once, when I needed money, Nitsos would not lend it to me, but Panayota gave me her own money. I had no reason to kill that good woman."

"So you still deny that you killed her?"

"I don't know how I can convince you. As I have said so many times before, I had no reason to kill her. I've been an orphan from my childhood, and I've struggled to find good husbands for my sisters and find a good wife for myself. I have always valued a family and a home. Why would I want to destroy someone else's home and family? I have never been found guilty of any crime in all my life. I have never bothered anybody. When I was made the village warden, I never used my authority to harm anyone. Only once have I ever had a run-in with somebody, and that was with Konandreas, and that man hates me. I arrested his son when he broke into the store and stole items worth four hundred drachmas. The entire village heard about this and how Konandreas threatened me at the time."

"What did he say?"

"He said, 'You'll pay for this,' and sure enough, he's making me pay now."

Thanasis shook his head in disgust. Once again, the truth was being distorted.

"Did Nitsos commit the murder?"

"I don't know what to say, Your Honor," Karaiskos answered with a shrug. "I have always known George Nitsos to be a good man, and I have known him for a good many years."

"Do you know who killed Panayota?"

"I don't know, but I'm sure Konandreas does. It could have been him or Vasilios or Panaitakis or one of the other Communists. They were probably trying to kill Nitsos and killed Panayota by mistake."

"Do you know that the shell found at the crime scene, according to the experts, came from your gun?"

"So I hear now. I don't know how the experts can say this. On that Tuesday afternoon after the murder, the captain of the county police asked me to fire three times into the ground. Then he asked Pantoulias, who was there, if the shells from the test shots matched the shell found at the crime scene. Pantoulias said they didn't. The captain then took all the shells and placed them all together on the school desk in front of him. The shell found at the crime scene was old and reloaded, and the one the captain sent to the interrogator was not. They were entirely different. The shell found at the crime scene wasn't fired from my gun."

"Why would the captain do that?"

"I don't know. Maybe he made a mistake."

"Why didn't you make a formal complaint that the shell was not from your gun? A year has passed since you were first arrested."

"My attorneys told me that my innocence would be clear when the forensic results came out."

"We don't want to be unjust to anybody," the prosecutor began, "especially not to an orphan and a poor person like you."

"It's because I'm an orphan that Konandreas did this to me," Socrates broke in. "He knows I can do nothing to defend myself."

"You say that Konandreas has a vendetta against you," the prosecutor began again. "But Konandreas did not even mention you as a suspect during his initial statement. And he asked you to dig the victim's grave. I cannot imagine he would be so sadistic."

"He hadn't yet made arrangements about who the witnesses would be, and that's why he didn't mention my name earlier. Now he's found people to lie for him against me. He's that kind of a man. He badly beat up a man some years back. He and I have had bad blood—everyone in Kupaki knows that."

"Listen, Karaiskos," the prosecutor said, "I'm obliged to point out some huge gaps in your statement, especially the fact that you haven't accounted for the time between nine-thirty p.m. and one a.m. on the night of the murder."

"Two hours are not enough to get to Kupaki and return to my hut," Socrates insisted. "And my gun that you keep talking about—it shoots wide of the mark four out of five times. Why would I depend on that gun to shoot and kill someone in the middle of the night? A moving target in the darkness, and a gun like that! If this wasn't a court, I'd think this was a bad joke."

CHAPTER 38:
AN ACT

DRESSED IN A LIGHT GRAY suit and black tie, his well-groomed hair combed back, George Nitsos took the witness stand looking as debonair as ever. Thanasis had seen his act before and was not in the least impressed by the man's outsized personality. Everyone else in the courtroom, even the prosecution attorneys, appeared seduced by the man's charm.

George gazed out at the faces staring back at him and, ignoring the prosecution's opening question, launched into a monologue. "I'm saddened," he said in a somber tone. "I'm saddened because I'm here, ladies and gentlemen, bearing the heavy accusation of being a wife-killer. This is why I ask you all now to listen carefully to my story—the story of an innocent man who for fourteen months has been dragging the cross of false accusation from detention house to detention house, from prison to prison.

"I come from a good family. My dream was to become a good family man. I married my wife in 1940 because I had been in love with her since 1936. Our wedding party lasted eight days. I lived with my wife in harmony. In 1940, I fought in the Greek army against the Italian invaders. During the German occupation in 1942, I was with the Nationalists while Konandreas was with the leftists."

"Nitsos!" the judge thundered. "I want you to talk about the murder!"

"I will, Your Honor," Nitsos said respectfully. "That's what I was getting to. I suffered greatly at the hands of the Communists. In 1946, I was serving with the National Guard, and it was at that time that I sent a letter to my wife Panayota and another to Poly. The letter I sent to Poly had nothing reproachable in it. I was answering a question she had asked me. She wanted to find out if the Academy of Pedagogy was located in the city where I was. I had made inquiries, and I wrote back to inform her of what I had learned. There was nothing terrible in the letter, contrary to what the witnesses here have said. None of them have read that letter; they have only heard gossip about it.

"In 1947, I came to live in Athens with my wife, who was suffering from swollen glands. We stayed until September of that year. I spent fifteen hundred dollars my parents had sent me from America on her treatment. Then I left Athens and returned to the village to fight the Communists until 1951. I was probably stupid, since I was the only one from the area to do that. The rest of the people stayed safe in Athens."

"We're conducting a murder trial in this courtroom, Nitsos," the judge said sternly, "not an inquiry into the civil war."

"During my service there," George continued, ignoring the judge's reprimand, "many Communists were beaten and exiled, which resulted in my making many enemies."

The judge intervened once more. "We're not writing the history of the civil war today. So tell us about September 6, 1953, the day your wife was murdered."

Palos, an attorney on the defense team, stood up. "Your Honor," he said, "I have to protest that the bench is restricting my client's rights to a free and fair trial by interrupting his statement. The entire defense team will have to leave the proceedings if this continues. I shall now leave the courtroom to register this protest."

He gathered his papers, tucked them under his arm, and marched out.

George, undeterred by the departure of one of his attorneys, continued on with his story. "On Sunday, September 6, 1953," he said, "I went to church with my wife. As the president of the church council, I was at the church counter by the register, selling candles. A little later, I took the donation tray around. Before the service was over, I stepped outside for a smoke. There Katina came to talk to me."

"What did you talk about?"

"I can't remember, but I remember that after the service, we went back home for lunch and then had a nap. Around four-thirty p.m., I went to my store, and my wife followed me later. She came to tell me that they had made arrangements for dinner that night with the Zakkases. She told me not to be late for it. I did go a little late, around eight-thirty p.m., and my wife had been there and had gone home. Before she left them, she had asked the Zakkases to call her when I got there so she could return. Indeed, my sister called her, and she came back. We ate, played cards—we actually played *Koumkan*—and at about ten-forty-five p.m., my wife told me that she was tired and wanted to leave. I asked her to stay a little longer so that I could finish the game. After the game, I got up to leave and asked my wife if she had remembered to bring a flashlight, but she told me that she had given it to our shepherd. I was ready to set out without a flashlight, but the others insisted and gave us one.

"The path starts to narrow from a point about twenty-to-thirty yards from the Zakkases'. That was where I held her beside me with my left arm, and I was shining the flashlight with my right hand. I was holding her on my left for support because my left foot was injured and I was limping. We walked about one hundred and sixty yards, and when we reached a curve in the path where the ravine is, we were shot at from the front. We moved backward a couple of steps, and we were shot at again. We fell down and started screaming. We were in great pain, and we were screaming, 'They're killing us!'

"Within seconds, Aggeliki Gumas appeared, holding a lamp. Her son John was with her. Her daughter, Konandreas's wife, followed soon after. They took us to the Gumases' front yard and called for a doctor. Panayota was saying, 'Vasilios has killed us.' I tried to help her, but then I felt sick and faint, so I moved further away, and then... she..."

What an act, Thanasis thought. The bastard was the only one from the entire village who did not cry when Panayota breathed her last outside the Gumases' house, and he was trying to do it here!

George took a moment to regain his composure in the packed courtroom, which had fallen silent in the wake of his teary performance.

When he appeared ready to continue, the prosecution resumed with its questions. "When did you take your wife back to your house?"

"After the doctor and the police chief from Krokylion got to Kupaki," George answered. "At about five o'clock the next morning, the captain from Krokylion took my statement. At about eleven a.m., the captain of the county police arrived. The chief of the local police, the county police captain, and a doctor of forensics who came from a nearby village to help, went with me to the crime scene, where the county police captain found an empty, fired shotgun shell. He began examining it. The doctor told him to be careful with the handling of the shell because the murderer could be traced from the fingerprints on that shell. On Monday afternoon, the county police captain called me to the house next door and asked me to help them find the killer. I told them that I wouldn't rest until I found the murderer. The captain

then asked me if I'd had any affairs with other women. He then
started writing some words of his own about my relationship with
Katina and—"

"How do you mean, 'words of his own'?" interrupted the judge.

The defense team complained about this interruption, but the
judge informed them that no vague or overstated statements would
go unchallenged.

"I told them that I had my suspicions about Vasilios, and especially
Poly's father," Nitsos continued. "The captain and I agreed that with
my help we would find the killer. On Tuesday morning, while the
church bells were ringing for my Panayota's funeral, the captain of
the county police ordered me to go to the school. I got there as fast
as I could, running part of the way. I asked the county police captain
what he wanted and pleaded with him to let me attend the funeral,
but to my surprise, he said that he was arresting me on suspicion of
the murder of my wife.

"I said, 'Me?' And he said, 'Sit down, keep quiet, and don't even
think about giving me any of your famous lip, because by the time I
finish with you, you'll be as still and silent as that two-thousand-pound
chest over there.' Even after my brother-in-law Zakkas mediated with
him to let me attend my wife's funeral, the captain did not relent.

"I was dumbstruck. I couldn't understand why the captain would
think that I would be stupid enough to murder my wife and hope
to get away with it. I have heard the things said about me in this
courtroom and in the Athenian dailies since this trial began, and I
don't expect any of you to believe that I loved my wife, but I did.

"Surely anybody can see that I haven't got up from a bed in a
mental hospital and walked here to give evidence. I'm of sound mind.
Why would someone like that kill his wife of fourteen years? If I
needed to get rid of her, couldn't I just go to America where I have
relatives? So many of them have been inviting me there for years!
And if I wanted to marry Katina, I could have done that so easily in
America. All I would have had to do was ask someone else to invite
her there and then marry her there.

"When I was commander of the band in my village, I could have
killed my wife a hundred times without any fear of repercussions. I
have been portrayed by the prosecution as a cunning man. Surely such
a cunning man wouldn't be naïve enough to solicit the murder of his
wife by auction, as it was presented to you. What sort of murderer
would go around publicly asking people to kill his wife for him?

"Konandreas," Nitsos continued, "was helping the police with their investigation, but what he was actually doing was buttering them up. Platter after platter of chicken arrived at the school from the Konandreas household when I was locked up there, and the policemen feasted on them. Konandreas was chatting with the police captain as though he was an officer himself.

"When they transferred us to Krokylion, Konandreas was immediately behind. From there they took us to the county capital, and he was at our heels. We ended up in the prefecture's capital. Konandreas arrived there by the first bus. He has been like a shadow ever since the murder.

"While we were in Prefecture's capital, he spread the rumor that we had confessed to the murder! There was nobody to support me or bother about my rights when I was locked up. My ex-partner never once came to see me. He was avoiding me not because I was guilty, but because he was guilty of using this opportunity for his financial ends. If he really suspected me for all these years, why would he have become my partner after—by his own admission—he found out that I was asking all and sundry to murder my wife?

"Contrary to what he now claims, he never wrote to my wife's relatives in Australia to take her there and save her from me because I was planning to kill her. Even when he gave his first statement, he didn't speak of George Nitsos as the murderer. Only after he went and made arrangements, paying money left, right, and center to Panaitakis and the other prosecution 'witnesses' did he begin spreading his nasty rumors. So many people have heard him doing that over the telephone. He has used every underhanded trick in the book that even hardened criminals would balk at.

"Why didn't he tell the police in 1946 when, according to him, he heard about my plans to kill Panayota? It's Konandreas who is the murderer, not me. It was he who planned to kill *me*. Only he ended up killing my wife. I want to remind you that at eleven p.m. that night Konandreas passed by the crime scene. How is it then that he did not see the killer who was lying in wait there? His wife was on the balcony of their house at the same time. Why was she there? What else could she have been doing there but waiting for the shots to be fired so that she could come and help her husband with his evil plan?

"At the same time, Konandreas's mother-in-law was staying up and looking out through her window. She says she was cleaning almonds. What—at eleven p.m.? It's obvious that all these people knew something was about to happen.

"There's no doubt that Konandreas is the pilot of the plot to incriminate me, but I'm not sure who else is with him on this. Only he knows that. It could be his shepherd, or Vasilios."

"Are you not aware, Nitsos," the prosecution attorney asked, "that Vasilios and Konandreas are not on good terms?"

"That's true, but they're both scoundrels, and when scoundrels see an opportunity, they bury the hatchet and become partners in crime."

"Why, then, did you become Konandreas's partner?" asked a prosecution attorney.

"I wanted to have the partnership with Pagonis but the building belonged to Konandreas's aunt and she wouldn't have let me have it any other way."

"Do you deny asking Panaitakis and Mary to help you murder Panayota?"

"That would have been the stupidest thing in the world. Ask the Panaitakis and Mary, indeed! They are such chatterboxes—worse than the radio—and no one in his right mind would confide in them. As the court has heard, the livestock that the three of us—Konandreas, Panaitakis, and I—jointly owned has disappeared. It's very clear to me that Mary and Panaitakis sold it for Panaitakis to support his gambling at poker."

"Are you suggesting that everyone who has given a statement against you in this courtroom is motivated by greed? Even the village priest, Papazois?" asked the prosecution.

"Papazois is a poor village priest waiting for the dollars from Konandreas's brother in America to marry off his two daughters," George said, waving off the question.

"In his initial statement, he called me a good man," George said. "Later, I became a killer!" George eyed the jury confidently before addressing the whole court.

"I challenge all those who accuse me. I challenge them to find a single reason for me to kill my wife. They say I'm a womanizer. I'm not denying that. Nobody's a saint. I certainly am not, but I'm not proud of my relationships with other women. I'm not the only adulterer in Greece. Many men cheat on their wives, but none of them leaves his wife for an easy woman. None of them murders his wife in order to have these relationships. Punish me for adultery, not for a murder I had no hand in.

"The witnesses for the prosecution have gone on and on here about Karaiskos, who has been my 'man' for a long time, who is willing to do any crime for me if the price is right. Why then did I comb the whole county, as they allege, for someone to murder my wife? Why not just ask Karaiskos in the first place to do it? Why did I not ask him in 1948 when he needed money badly to marry off his sisters?

"Karaiskos is a good man, and if I were to ask him to commit a murder for five hundred sovereigns, he would go straight to the police and tell them that Nitsos is up to no good. Besides, Karaiskos would have never harmed Panayota. He loved and respected her."

"Why didn't you show any interest in chasing the killer after the murder?" the prosecution asked. "Doesn't it suggest that you knew the murderer, and catching him would lead the investigation right to your door?"

"I don't know how many people here have tried chasing someone when they have been shot and injured and are in pain and losing blood. I was feeling weak and shaky and sick, and it was too dark to give chase, anyway. Besides, how could I go and find a killer whose identity I didn't know?"

"Isn't it true that you prevented Katina from going to America? Does that seem like the action of a man who didn't have any deep feelings for the woman with whom he was cheating on his wife?"

"I never told Katina not to go to America. All I said was, 'Why do you want to go to America? To clean dishes?' And that has been made into a big thing here.

"Now the gun shell that was found at the crime scene," George continued, "that's not the one presented here in court as evidence. The substitution was probably done by accident or deliberately by Panaitakis, Konandreas, or the captain."

"Why didn't you bring this up earlier?" an attorney from the prosecution team asked. "My attorneys will answer that question," George replied arrogantly.

The courtroom fell silent, and George, no doubt sensing an opportunity, quickly took the initiative.

"Your Honor, respected members of the jury," he said, "I'm alien to these false accusations leveled against me. You see before you a totally innocent, misunderstood man who has lost the wife he loved and now pleads for his own life and freedom that his enemies have taken away from him. I request that you let me have them back. I'm innocent, and I hope you will return a verdict of not guilty."

CHAPTER 39:
THE 9:1 VERDICT

ON NOVEMBER 12, 1954, ON a cool, misty evening, Thanasis took his seat beside the prosecution and waited. The clock read a quarter past eight when the judge entered from his chambers. The courtroom, filled beyond capacity, buzzed with anticipation. Tonight the jury would decide on a verdict. Tonight George Nitsos and Socrates Karaiskos would be sentenced or go free. The two men, until now the embodiment of bravado, sunk into their seats. Their anxiety was palpable.

"Let me remind each member of the jury of the solemn oath that you've taken," the judge began.

As soon as the judge was through addressing them, the jury disappeared behind closed doors to deliberate. Thanasis watched as audience members spun around in their chairs to discuss the case with others nearby. Seconds ticked by slowly, agonizingly.

Thanasis looked at Papaskevi, Panayota's mother, who remained in her seat. Silent, immobile—she sat perfectly still, save for her gnarled old hands, which were hard at work on a black handkerchief, now twisted in knots. Every few minutes, she paused in her work as her eyes darted furtively toward the door behind which the jury continued to deliberate.

Finally, at three a.m., after nearly seven hours of debate, the jury returned.

The jury foreman stepped forward.

Silence fell over the courtroom.

"With honor and conscience," he announced, "I declare the verdict of the lawful majority of the jury." He paused to clear his throat.

Thanasis felt his heart race. For several days now, he had feared the jury was corrupt, but maybe he was wrong. Maybe the men had deliberated this long because someone among them had argued the facts. Maybe the truth had won.

"We find the defendants," the foreman said, "not guilty."

The people were instantly on their feet, their collective roar nearly swallowing the foreman's pronouncement. Some shouted in joy. Others gesticulated wildly from anger. A month's worth of testimony had been whittled down to seven hours of deliberation, which in turn had been squeezed into one grave pronouncement. George Nitsos and Socrates Karaiskos would go free.

Thanasis searched the courtroom until his gaze fell on Papaskevi, Panayota's mother. She was staring back at him, her eyes lost in confusion. It wasn't until she saw the look on his face—he could only imagine how disappointed he looked—that she appeared to understand what had happened. And as her countenance fell, he saw the same misery in her eyes, the same utter devastation, that he had seen back in Kupaki, in the Gumases' courtyard, on the night of the murder, when she had collapsed and tore at her clothes. She clamped her jaw shut, drawing her lips into a thin line, but was unable to stop the forlorn wail that rose from deep within her battered heart.

The moment the furor abated in the courtroom, the public prosecutor, asked the judge's permission to speak.

"Your Honor," he began, "the jury's decision doesn't agree with the evidence that came to light from detailed deliberations. I request that the court find this decision *peplanimeni*, so that the case can be decided by another trial at a later date, which will be determined by the attorney general."

Gunaris shot to his feet for the defense. "We request the court reject the public prosecutor's appeal," he said. "Accepting it would be tantamount to disgracing the rule of law and the institution of jurors."

The judge deliberated for fifteen minutes, and at half-past three in the morning, he announced the court's acceptance of the prosecutor's appeal.

A few hours later, after a fitful bit of rest, a tired and battered Thanasis dragged himself out of bed and went to meet with the prosecution team. What he and his attorneys learned after reading accounts from two different dailies only confirmed his suspicions that the jury had been corrupt.

The behind-the-scenes reporting of the court reporter for *Vradini* showed how the jury had come to vote nine to one in favor of the defense—and how the defense had been privy to that information before the verdict had been issued:

Defense attorney Palos carelessly revealed a secret that he wasn't supposed to know. While congratulating the jurors for their verdict, he expressed his disappointment that one juror had voted against the majority and had therefore given the right to the public prosecutor to ask the court for a hung jury. Following that, during the judge's deliberations of the public prosecutor's proposal, I was assured that the jurors made it known in the corridors of the courthouse that indeed there had been one vote for the minority and that the vote in question had been produced by the juror who was not approaching the others...

The lone juror who was not approaching the others was Demosthenes Dapontes.

"Palos wasn't supposed to know that, was he?" Thanasis asked his attorneys. "Am I not correct in thinking that only the judge and the public prosecutor were allowed at that point to know the balance of votes? So who leaked the information to the defense? They must all be in cahoots with each other—the defense team and the jury. What a farce!"

"What's done is done," a bleary-eyed Tsukalas said. "Let's concentrate on building a solid case for next time."

Thanasis sat back in his chair and let go an exhausted sigh. He couldn't imagine enduring a second trial. He was painfully aware of the pressure he would face from family and friends to drop the whole thing. They would tell him that such a foolhardy enterprise was a waste—and would cut into what little money he had saved for his children's future. Worse still, he knew he didn't have a counter argument to give them. They were right.

Stymied by his own sense of duty, Thanasis stood up.

"Where are you going?" Tsukalas asked. "We still have much to discuss."

"I need to telegram my wife before the newspapers reach Krokylion. She should hear the news from her husband, not some village gossip."

At the village, while George's and Socrates's supporters celebrated the news proclaiming the two men innocent, those of us who had supported the prosecution weren't quite sure how to respond. *Peplanimeni* didn't roll off the tongue nearly as easily as *guilty*. Would there be another trial? Would George and Socrates ever be punished? Far from providing any sense of resolution, the month-long trial in Athens had merely given us more of what we had already endured: more questions, more indecision, and more waiting.

CHAPTER 40:
FAMILY PRESSURES

"How could those jurors overlook all that evidence and rule 'not guilty'?" Mitros kept asking.

"I wish I knew," Thanasis answered with a sigh.

"What did those wretches say?" asked Mitros, who wasn't ready to give up.

"The jurors? Well, their foreman said that 'with honor and conscience' they could say that Nitsos and Karaiskos aren't guilty."

"Honor and conscience, indeed!" Mitros spat.

Thanasis could do nothing to appease the old man. It had been the same with everyone since his return to the village a few days earlier. Family members, friends, and fellow villagers had suffocated him with their questions. All anyone wanted to know about was how the jury could have possibly come to its decision.

Gradually they had given up, but Mitros, ever dogged, had continued with his badgering. The disbelief in his tone told Thanasis that his uncle had no intention of letting go anytime soon.

—————◦⁓◦—————

On the day of *Apokreon*, the beginning of Advent, which followed soon, my mouth watered as my parents made preparations for a holiday feast of roast lamb with potatoes and cheese pie, all of which would be roasted over the embers of a wood fire. Also on the menu were the usual suspects: feta cheese, olives, and red wine.

Papazois and Papadia arrived with their two daughters just before meal time, followed shortly by Aunt Aggelo and her two children. We crowded around the table, and soon we were pleasantly stuffed.

After dinner, Thanasis fed a cheerful fire with another huge log. While my brothers and I played nearby, the adults talked about the good old times, before the murder. It seemed that even now, in the warmth of our home, surrounded by beloved family, none of us could escape the courtroom back in Athens. The verdict was like an uninvited guest who insisted on making his presence felt.

"Hoy, hoy," Grandma Efthemia said with a heavy sigh. "What are we going to do now?"

She looked at Thanasis the way Polyxeni often looked at me when she disapproved of something I'd done. "I want you to stop, to give up the trial and stay with your family. Let those bastards go to hell or wherever the devil takes them."

Papadia and Aggelo gave encouraging nods.

"Is this what you think I should do?" Thanasis asked, clearly taken aback.

"Yes!" the women answered without hesitation.

Papazois, who had been silent so far, spoke up. "Listen, Thanasis," he said gently. "You have done more than your share. You can't leave everything else and spend the rest of your life and money in the courts."

"It's not as though you haven't done enough for your cousin," Polyxeni said, having waited patiently for her turn to speak. "But how much more can anyone expect from you?"

Father listened silently as he moved one of the logs in the fireplace with a poker.

Finally Grandma Efthemia had had enough. "What are you doing?" she demanded. "Playing with the fire? Stop that right now. Say something!"

"What do you want me to say?" he asked with a shrug. "Do you want to let the bastards who killed your niece walk free? Do you want to live the rest of your life with the knowledge that you walked away from a chance to seek justice for Panayota?"

"Panayota has many other cousins," Papadia, responded. "They are men, too, and none of them has taken this to such extremes."

"We all understand your problem, Thanasis," Aunt Aggelo said. "Nobody wants to let the murderers go free, but we need to go on with our lives."

"Let's suppose I give up," Thanasis said. "Do you think that I or any of you will have peace and quiet if Linatsas comes back to Kupaki? Have you forgotten about him?"

No one uttered a reply.

"Even inside the court," Thanasis said, pressing the issue, "he was behaving in his usual devil-may-care way. Do you think a man like that will change? He will go around challenging us and mocking us, until we take the law into our own hands."

Mother's face darkened. "Look," she said, pointing at my siblings and me. "Look at these children when you feel all that pride and bravado and vengefulness. Don't you realize they'll become orphans and you'll be in jail? Go! Go after those killers if you have to—and be a killer yourself!"

"Do you really think I enjoy this?" Father asked meekly.

"Well, if you don't," Papadia said, "why don't you just stay home?"

Thanasis dropped the poker with a clang and sank into his chair. "If this is what you all want," he said in a defeated voice, "what else can I do? I'll simply have to give up."

Everyone seemed to be relieved to hear this, even the children, who had long ago stopped playing to listen to the conversation, but I wasn't. I wanted Thanasis to continue on in his quest for justice.

Later that night, long after the last of our guests had gone home, Grandma Efthemia cursed and ranted in her sleep. Like the rest of us, she was still devastated by the verdict. As someone who had once been a staunch supporter of Thanasis's efforts, she seemed to have given up on justice for Panayota—and wanted Thanasis to do the same.

Would he? Would Grandma and Mother and everyone else succeed in tying his hands? As I drifted off to sleep, I hoped somehow Thanasis would find the courage and strength to continue the fight.

Thanasis was already awake the next morning when Polyxeni began stirring.

"What we said last night can't be done," he said as soon as she was fully awake. "I have to finish what I started."

She propped herself up on one elbow and stared back at him with a faint smile that hinted at pride, tenderness and a tint of regret. "You're going to continue, right?" she said softly.

"I knew it. I know you."

CHAPTER 41:
THE ATTORNEY GENERAL

"Do you have an appointment?" an official at the attorney general's office asked. "Is the attorney general expecting you?"

Thanasis, dressed in a clean suit and standing erect in the reception office, looked directly into the man's eyes, determined to portray dignity as well as doggedness. "No," he said. "But I have traveled all the way from my village to see him."

In fact, Thanasis had been quite busy of late. While others in the village had drifted lazily toward the inevitable winter hibernation, spending the shrinking daylight hours indoors curled up beside the fireplace, Thanasis had been busily laying the groundwork for a second trial.

Although he had kindly refused an offer from Uncle Mitros to write him into his will—a generous but ultimately futile offer, considering he needed money *now*, not in ten or twenty years—he had written his brother in America and had received the promise of one thousand American dollars, along with a letter of encouragement containing an emboldening rallying cry: *Go after the bastards.*

He had then traveled to the courthouse in the city of Patras, where George had spent time in his youth. There he had learned that, despite the turmoil of the civil war, records still existed of George's arrest there so long ago. Next, he had met with Kokkinos, his local attorney, and asked about George's record as well as funding for witnesses. Wasn't it possible, he had asked, to get the Department of Justice to cover his witnesses' expenses if the judiciary summoned said witnesses? Kokkinos, clearly impressed that Thanasis had done his homework, had nevertheless warned him that he would need authorization from the attorney general—no easy thing to secure.

Now, with Christmas just around the corner, Thanasis was

standing in the attorney general's outer office and politely demanding a meeting with him.

"What's your name?" another official asked. By now, Thanasis had drawn a small crowd of curious officials.

"Thanasis Konandreas."

"Which village did you say you're from?"

"I'm from Kupaki, near Lidoriki."

"This man Konandreas came from Kupaki and thinks he can see the attorney general," a guard standing nearby said in mocking tones to his fellow sentry.

"Did you say Konandreas from Kupaki?" a man asked as he entered the building.

The guards parted to make room for the man, a middle-aged gentleman dressed in a well-tailored suit.

"Yes," Thanasis answered.

"Are you not from the big trial with Nitsos and Karaiskos?"

"Yes."

"He wants to see the attorney general," one of the guards said, "but we're trying to explain to him that that's impossible."

"Stay here, Mr. Konandreas," the official said and disappeared inside the office.

He was back within minutes. "General Konstandinides will see you now," he announced.

Inside the stately office, General Konstandinides came out from behind his desk to welcome Thanasis with an extended hand. "A pleasure, Mr. Konandreas, a pleasure!" he said enthusiastically. "I wish Greece had more Greeks like you!"

Thanasis, surprised by the warm reception, managed to mutter his thanks and sink into the plush chair that the attorney general offered him.

"What can I do for you?"

"I'm a cousin of Panayota Nitsos, who was—"

"I know the whole case, Mr. Konandreas. Why else do you think I said I wished we had more Greeks like you? Now tell me what I can do for you."

"The prosecution needs several witnesses for the second trial," Thanasis said, still shocked that he had received such an unexpected welcome from the attorney general. "I was wondering if they could be summoned by the judiciary. You see, I have spent the best part of my meager savings on fighting this case, and now—"

"Let me have the names," General Konstandinides said, interrupting him once again. "I'll summon them, and I'll ask the ministry for a special daily rate, by which the prosecution witnesses can be reimbursed for their expenses."

"Thank you."

"Is there anything else?"

"Well, there is one more thing," Thanasis answered cautiously. "I need to locate some old court records, which I believe show that about twenty years ago George Nitsos was taken to court for theft—and was found guilty."

General Konstandinides immediately summoned his clerks. "I want all the information we have on George Nitsos of Kupaki."

While his subordinates were searching the archives, Konstandinides told Thanasis that his department had been working hard to ensure that the events of the first trial would not repeat themselves.

"We have decided to have the second trial in Halkida, where criminal justice has traditionally been strong. We have never had any problems with people playing the system there. The jury there will be beyond reproach. I don't want the trial to be in a city where the proximity to Kupaki could mean unwelcome political influence."

"I have no experience with such things, sir," Thanasis said modestly. "If this is what you think is best, I will go with it."

"Good man. I will appoint the most upright judges for the trial and ensure that the jury will be chosen from the most educated people of Halkida, who are also economically and politically independent and therefore unapproachable by any outside influences."

While Thanasis was savoring the unexpected stroke of good fortune, the attorney general's subordinates returned to say that no records on Nitsos existed and, though they could be in Patras, where the offense had taken place, they had most likely been destroyed due to their age.

"I have been to Patras looking for that record," Thanasis responded quickly, before the attorney general could reply, "and I was told that the records from that time in 1934 exist."

"If such a record exists," Konstandinides said, "I promise you that my department will make it available at the trial in Halkida."

Thanasis thanked the attorney general and stood up to leave.

"Mr. Konandreas." Konstandinides's voice stopped him at the door. "The law will take its course, and the attorney general must remain impartial while it does, but I wish you all success.If there is anything I can do, do not hesitate to get in touch."

"Thank you, sir," Thanasis said appreciatively. "I hope your wish comes true."

PART V

CHAPTER 42:
TO HALKIDA FOR JUSTICE?

ABOUT A WEEK BEFORE CHRISTMAS 1954, news arrived that the trial would take place in Halkida, the capital of the island of Evia, with the first hearing to be heard on March 8 of 1955.

When Thanasis contacted Kokkinos and Tsukalas, they advised him to hire another attorney, someone from Halkida who was familiar with the court, its judges, its attorneys, and its ways.

Though Thanasis received a check for a thousand dollars from Kutras, his brother in America, along with wishes for much success, he was wondering how he was going to pay a third attorney and the expenses for all the prosecution witnesses in a city in which he knew nobody and had never visited.

As the swallows began to fly over Kupaki signaling the coming of spring, thirty men and women left the village to appear in court. March 10, 1955, marked the first day of the trial in Halkida, a city of 25,000 renowned for its seaside beauty. The great Greek philosopher Aristotle had spent a substantial part of his life in Halkida, his mother's hometown, as had numerous physicists intent on solving the unique tidal phenomenon of its waters. Affectionately known as "the bride of the Evoikos Gulf," Halkida spanned the mainland as well as Evia Island and was connected by a series of bridges.

Thanasis and the other witnesses arrived early on March 10th at the courthouse, an early 20th-century neoclassical building. Ionian columns decorated the entrance, where a marble statue of Andreas Syngros, the man whose philanthropy had funded the building's construction stood. Evergreens dotted the courtyard, as did benches, already occupied by the visitors.

As soon as the door was opened, the group moved inside, and Thanasis, one of the first to enter, spotted an enormous crucifix hanging above the farthest wall and just over the judge's bench.

Judge Argyrios Demopoulos called the court to order and proceeded to select the jurors along with the public prosecutor, Limberis Papandreou. Ten jurors and two alternates were picked, and their ranks included four attorneys, a professional with a legal background, three industrialists, a schoolteacher, a retired police officer, a pharmacist, and a merchant. The defense team, meanwhile, was headed up by two local attorneys.

Thanasis, the first witness, strode to the front of the court in a dark jacket, white shirt, and black tie. After repeating much of his testimony from the previous trial, he told the jury that George had once sent Panayota to a nearby town and had planned to kill her en route with the help of a right-wing extremist group.

"Linatsas also tried to talk a dentist into killing Panayota by mixing poison with the dental anesthetic shot," he said. "The dentist refused and informed Nick, a dance instructor."

"Why didn't you propose this Nick as a witness?" Papandreou, the public prosecutor, asked.

"I couldn't get him to be a witness since he's related to Linatsas."

Kokkinos moved on to the subject of Katina and her affair with Nitsos.

"Katina was having sex with Nitsos", Thanasis said, "and in return he bought her the things she wanted: a watch, shoes, a handbag. And he took precautions to hide their relationship. At Lidoriki, where she was a high school student, Nitsos pretended that she was his niece. Also, Katina had plans to emigrate to Canada, but Nitsos, who as village president had to issue papers and certificates, withheld all her papers."

"Why was he stopping her from leaving?" Papandreou asked.

"He wanted her for himself."

After Papandreou finished with his questions, an attorney by the name of Karamitros took up the cross-examination. "I put it to you, Thanasis Konandreas, that young people have relationships that don't necessarily end in marriage. Can you explain why you felt duty bound, as you claim, to ensure that George Nitsos married your cousin Panayota Soulias just because he had slept with her?"

"That was not the issue. Nitsos promised Panayota to marry her.

She slept with him because of this promise. This was a question of a broken promise. That is why I pressured Nitsos to marry Panayota."

"I further ask you," Karamitros said, "that divorced women no longer feel alienated as they used to do, even in more traditional areas of Greece like your village. Therefore, the claim that Panayota would be humiliated if Nitsos divorced her is patently a non-issue that has been made into an issue by the prosecution."

"Counsel," Thanasis said, "let's not forget that we're both from neighboring villages. I'm from Kupaki, and you're from the village across the river from mine, and you have close ties with Kupaki as a relative of Nitsos's brother-in-law Zakkas. If one of your city-bred colleagues had put that argument to me, I would have at least thought that they believe in that nonsense. You should know better. Tell me: how many divorced women do you know in our area who live a normal life in their communities without any alienation and humiliation? We both know the families in the area. Whisper to me if you feel uncomfortable naming names in public."

Karamitros retreated, visibly deflated.

"The witness is smart," Judge Demopoulos muttered just loud enough to be heard.

"That he is," agreed Pan Gunaris, another attorney on the defense team. "Had he not been, he would be where the accused are sitting now."

That night at the Euripus Hotel, where the prosecution witnesses were staying, Thanasis coached Papaskevi, Panayota's mother, who was slated to take the witness stand the next day.

"I know you can't help feeling a little intimidated at the sight of all the slick attorneys and the judge and the packed courtroom," he said gently, "but you need to let them see how much loss you feel. You're much more than just a village woman. Show them the strength inside you. You're a mother who lost her daughter. Let those people see how that loss makes you feel. Show that in your words. Show that in your actions."

Thanasis saw the fruits of his coaching the next morning in court, when Paraskevi launched into a litany of curses against George and Socrates the moment she was called to the witness stand. Several minutes were needed for the judge to calm her down, but eventually he was able to steer her toward a calmer discussion.

"Nitsos mistreated my daughter," she said, "not because she didn't give him children, but because of all the other women he was carrying on with. I saw my daughter tormented and bitter, but she kept everything inside and never complained.

"She wanted to spare me, and I burned inside because I knew what it was costing her to do that. Once in my presence, that man threw her plates and glasses onto the floor and shouted, 'If your mother weren't here, I would have beaten you black and blue!'"

Without pausing for a breath, Paraskevi pointed a finger at Nitsos and once again raised her voice. "You devil of... you sent her where I will never see her again! At times my daughter had to sleep outside her own house. You even brought one of your whores to that house. That was why lightning hit your house and you fell and broke your leg." Paraskevi turned to Judge Demopoulos. "And my daughter lived through all this. Kupaki is so small that everyone would get to know if she left her husband. It would have been a big humiliation to be the only woman in the village to be estranged from her husband."

George stood. "May I ask the witness a question, Your Honor?"

"Sit down, Nitsos," the judge snapped, "before you make a big blunder."

"I insist, Your Honor."

"Very well, then."

"In 1944," Nitsos began, "did I not send your daughter to Athens to get treatment for her stomach troubles? Do you remember how long that was for? Would I have done that if all the lies you say about me were true?"

"You're going to ask me questions now?" Paraskevi shot back. "You sent her there to get rid of her, you bastard, so that you could have fun with your whores."

Judge Demopoulos shook his head at George. "I did tell you that you were going to make a blunder, did I not?"

On March 10 after the afternoon session had begun at school, I approached, my new teacher with an unusual request.

"My grandmother wants me to go and get a newspaper from Krokylion," I said.

No doubt eager to know the news from the trial in Halkida, the teacher didn't hesitate to grant me his permission.

I hurried home, dropped off my school bag and, after receiving two drachmas from my grandmother, raced down the steps into the yard.

"Hey, you!"

I skidded to a halt and turned to see Mitros, my great-uncle.

"If you're going for a newspaper," he said, handing me a few coins, "get me one, too."

"Grandma Efthemia gave me the money, *Papu*," I replied impatiently. I was eager to get to Krokylion before the papers sold out.

"I want my own paper," he harrumphed.

"But, *Papu*, you can't read. What are you going to do with it?"

"Well, that grandmother of yours can't read, either," he said grumpily.

Realizing it was foolish to argue any further, I quietly pocketed the two drachmas and took off for Krokylion.

In Krokylion, amidst the buzzing crowd at the shop, I managed to buy copies of the *Kathimerini* and the *Ethnos*. I was back home before sunset.

Soon my brothers and I were huddled around the fireplace with our grandmother.

Mitros arrived just as we were ready to read the papers. "Where is my newspaper?" he demanded.

"Here it is, *Papu*," I said and handed him a paper. "But who will read it for you?"

Mitros, who hadn't been to the house since his last argument with Efthemia, fell silent.

Grandma, in a surprise move, stood up, grabbed a stool, and carried it to the other side of the fireplace. "Sit there," she said dryly.

Mitros hesitated. I could tell by his furrowed brow that he wasn't sure he could trust this olive branch from Grandma Efthemia, but he eventually accepted the offer and took a seat beside us boys. This, I knew from past experience, was the beginning of an unofficial truce between the two warring elders, and it would likely last just until the next difference of opinion between them sparked another quarrel.

We recognized Judge Demopoulos in a photo that accompanied one of the articles. He and the public prosecutor had been in Kupaki only a few days earlier to inspect the crime scene.

As I skimmed a section in the *Kathimerini*, skipping most of the names of the jurors and whatnot, I came to a passage about Thanasis and the answers he was giving to the judge's questions.

Mitros, though, wanted to know more about the jury. "Read that bit about the jurors to me again," he said. "Does it list their names and occupations?"

Efthemia, of course, wanted only to hear about what her son had said in Halkida. "No," she said. "Keep reading about Thanasis."

For a moment, I feared the two would come to blows,but just as quickly as their tempers flared, Mitros lowered his voice.

"Thanasis said they promised in Athens they will have good jurors this time. I just need to find out what sort of jury they've got there," he said in a reasonable tone.

"Fine," Efthemia shot back. "Go ahead, then."

"D. Tsokos, industrialist," I said, reading the first name.

"Good!" Mitros shouted his approval.

"N. Vamvakulas, merchant," I continued.

"Keep going," the old man answered.

"P. Kulopoulos, attorney."

"Yes!" he shouted.

"K. Karros, retired military officer," I read.

"*Yeeeeees!*" he responded uncorking the word in one long howl. He was on his feet now, his eyes twinkling brightly. With each new name read, his triumphant shouts grew louder.

By the time I had finished reading the twelfth name, Mitros was hollering like a teenager whose favorite soccer team had just scored the winning goal at the World Cup.

"Atta boy!" he shouted. "Now we have them! Nothing can save them!"

Efthemia, too, was overjoyed by the news, and the two rivals began discussing the jurors and rejoicing in the hope that the jury would hear the case fairly this time, unaffected by the influence of money or politics.

"How many times have you been a juror in court?" Efthemia asked Mitros. "Did you talk to those judges when they came here?"

Soon our teacher arrived.

"What do you think the outcome of this new trial will be?" the teacher asked Mitros.

"I predict that we'll win," my great-uncle replied confidently. "I haven't the slightest doubt about it. What about you?"

"You could be right," the teacher replied in a cautious voice. "Anyway, I'm going to wait before I say anything."

CHAPTER 43:
"STRAIGHT IN THE VILLAGE, CROOKED IN COURT."

SUNDAY MORNING, MARCH 13, DAWNED brightly, and as my parents walked along the waterfront in Halkida, Polyxeni spotted a handful of witnesses for the defense walking in the opposite direction along the promenade. Back in Kupaki, she thought, the opposing sides took any opportunity to have it out with their rivals, but here, in this seaside town, the witnesses appeared weighed down by the burden of representation. They were staying in nearby hotels—the prosecution at the Euripus Hotel and the defense at the Ekali Hotel. And not only did they have to testify to the truth on the witness stand but also they were responsible for representing their village. Everything they did in the big city would reflect back on Kupaki. So whenever the groups met, as they often did on the seafront, they studiously avoided confrontation, limiting their interaction to harmless statements about the weather; the conveniences in their hotels, which sat just two hundred yards apart from one another; and the sights of the city.

Church bells echoed nearby, and Mother instantly thought of St. George and its cracked walls back home. Dozens of young children hurried by on their way to a nearby church, and as they did, Mother's thoughts turned to my siblings and me. Normally she was the one to lead us in a line to our village's church for Sunday services. Mother also heard some young people by the courthouse singing a sad melody, which was sympathetic to the plight of the defendants:

> *Come, Mother, to see this son of yours*
> *Come, cry with him and feel his sorrows*
> *Within these prison walls I languish*

Imprisoned by injustice and anguish

Thanasis frowned. He knew the people in the city were very sympathetic to his cause. Many were stopping and encouraging him outside the court and in the streets.

"I'm going to take this matter to my local attorney," he said. "He needs to find out who these people going around singing this stupid song are. The prosecution ought to be able to do something about this!"

Little did he know that fifty years later, on a hot August evening in Halkida's St. Nicholas square, I would encounter the very same song, this time sung by an old man when I visited while researching this book.

Panaitakis was called to the witness stand the next morning and repeated much of what he had said at the trial in Athens.

Thanasis looked on as the defense presented a letter, allegedly sent from a villager from Kupaki, which contained statements contradicting those made by Panaitakis. Without waiting for the letter to be admitted by the court, the defense then asked the judge to delay the proceedings so they could have time to summon the other villager.

The prosecution objected to the reading of the letter, which infuriated the defense.

"Objection!" Palos snapped angrily. "You're denying us the opportunity to find the killer. Konandreas has committed the crime, and we're not allowed to prove it!"

"If the defense attorney knows more than the evidence has shown so far," Papandreou, the public prosecutor, replied, "he should appear as a witness. It would be my privilege to question him then. Otherwise, he should stop scattering baseless accusations about."

"I'm a bit strapped for cash now," Thanasis said, addressing the prosecution witnesses one evening in the lobby of the Euripus Hotel. "I can continue paying for your food, room, and board. So for the time being, if you can use your own money for other expenses, I promise to reimburse you."

He eyed the others hopefully. Would they agree? The trial, still far from finished, had already eaten up the American dollars sent to him from Kutras. Having been forced to dip into his savings, he knew he wouldn't be able to pay his witnesses' expenses much longer, especially with substantial hotel bills and attorney's fees still due. At the trial in Athens, they had managed to crowd many of the witnesses into the Gumas house and at the homes of other friends and family members. But free board and lodging wasn't an option in Halkida.

To Thanasis's great relief, the witnesses all agreed to pay their own way—for now, anyway.

Mary, who was on the witness stand next, was asked by a juror, "Why didn't Nitsos murder his wife himself by pushing her down from the oak tree or over the cliff from her horse? Why did he need to ask you for help?"

"He is a coward!"

"Besides Konandreas," Kokkinos asked, "to whom did you reveal Nitsos's request to you and to your husband to kill Panayota?"

"To another one of Panayota's cousins and Socrates Karaiskos."

"Why did you have to make this revelation to Karaiskos?" the judge asked in surprise.

"I had an argument with Nitsos," Mary answered, "and I was angry with him at the time. I asked Karaiskos: 'Why did Linatsas cut the water we use to irrigate our fields and give it to another villager? Is it because we didn't kill his wife?' Of course, Karaiskos reported this to Nitsos, because later, when my husband went to see him, Nitsos told him, 'Your wife told Karaiskos that I tried to kill my wife.' My husband saved me by saying, 'Oh, don't give any notice to women's talk.'"

The court wanted to know how and when Mary had spoken to Karaiskos, since her testimony contradicted his.

Thanasis, who had been instructed by the judge to be available at the front of the courtroom to answer questions when needed, thought about how he could clarify the disagreement between Mary and Karaiskos. He offered to speak to the judge privately. The judge replied that in his court there would be no secrets and refused. Defense attorney Palos then stated that Thanasis's offer reflected the secret strategy of the prosecution. He then called Thanasis the murderer.

This infuriated Thanasis, who asked the court to protect him. Papandreou, the public prosecutor, intervened and offered Thanasis the opportunity to sue Palos in this present court, which Thanasis did. Palos then accused Papandreou of bias, and heated exchanges followed between the two men.

Nearly lost in all of Tuesday's combustible behavior was the testimony of a shepherd who worked for Thanasis. He said that in August 1952, he went from his village to Kupaki to meet with George Nitsos. He owed George some money and arrived at his home intending to make good on his debt, but it was George who was offering to pay *him* money.

"He said, 'I will give you one hundred sovereigns if you kill a person I have in my house,' and I answered, 'George, 'I don't do these kinds of things.' When he realized I was not the man for such a job, he replied, 'It was a joke.' A couple of months later, I asked Konandreas what relationship he had with George's wife, and he said she was his cousin. I told him then what George had asked me to do."

On Wednesday, March 16, Harry repeated the testimony he had given at the trial in Athens. He was a villager who reportedly had been solicited to murder Panayota.

"Why did everybody go to Konandreas and not to the police when they knew Nitsos was planning the murder?" the defense asked. "And why did Konandreas himself not go to the police?"

The judge called upon Thanasis to answer.

"As I have said many times before," Thanasis said, "I didn't go to the police because I didn't believe that Nitsos was really going to kill his wife, but it was also because of Panayota. She wouldn't let me go to the police, either."

Thanasis Konandreas, left, argues with George Nitsos in court, March 16, 1955. Harry, a prosecution witness, center, stares straight ahead.

"Was Panayota herself willing to help you and act against her husband?" Papandreou asked.

"She always wanted to work things out amicably," Thanasis explained. "She loved Nitsos, and she didn't even want to hear about divorce. She was also a bit conceited on some matters involving her relationship with her husband. To illustrate this point, I want to tell you about the time I wrote to her brother and sister in New Zealand about their problems. After that, Panayota wrote back to them saying that the things written to them were all lies. She loved that man."

"But do you see what happened in the end?" a juror asked.

"I do. Several people from the village told me to forcefully mediate a divorce. But I didn't want to be known as the family breaker in Kupaki."

A defense attorney, joined in. "If you had told Nitsos to get a divorce, would that have been for the better or for the worse?"

"I had no way of knowing it at the time, but it would definitely have been for the better," Thanasis answered. "I would probably have argued with Nitsos and split the business I had with him, but we could probably have avoided the terrible thing that happened later."

"Were you not afraid that Panayota would tell Nitsos that you had told her that he was planning to kill her?" a juror, asked.

"I was not. Their relationship was like the one between cats and dogs."

George Nitsos stood up and faced the court. His question, though, was aimed directly at Thanasis. "How come he didn't tell my mother-in-law these things? He has turned that woman into a rag now."

Thanasis felt his jaw harden. "Listen to what he's saying." He turned to face George. "You took care of the old woman very well, didn't you? You killed her daughter. Now just leave her alone."

A photographer from the *Acropolis*, busily clicking away, captured the exchange between the two men. His photo would run on the front page the next day.

Polyxeni Konandreas, who took the stand next, spoke about the terrible way George had treated Panayota, and soon George was once again protesting to the court.

"Your Honor," he said, feigning injury, "I want to complain that this witness is lying."

"What I speak is the truth," Polyxeni responded calmly. "There isn't a single lie here."

"You're a slave in your house," George snapped, "while in mine, my wife was the queen!"

"If I work like a slave, I do it for my own family," Polyxeni retorted, "but you exiled your 'queen' to a place from which she will never come back!"

Papandreou took over before George could muster a reply. "Did you hear Panayota say to Alexandra the words, 'Now that you have devoured me'?"

"I was getting my horse ready during Panayota's last moments so that someone could ride to Krokylion for a doctor," Polyxeni said. "So I didn't hear those words, but my sister-in-law Aggelo says that she did."

Papandreou turned to the jurors. "Gentlemen," he said, "you've heard the witness. The defense has been telling you that Konandreas has been coaching the witnesses for the prosecution to lie against the accused. This woman is Konandreas's wife, and even she doesn't seem to have been coached by him, as all of you can judge from what she just said. If she had been coached, she would have said that she did hear those words."

During the afternoon session, Vasilios repeated his testimony from the Athens trial.

When asked by the judge what the public opinion was at the village, he gave a simple answer. "Judge," he said, "a case straight in the village, crooked in court."

His words were immortalized in the newspapers the next day.

CHAPTER 44:
IS THIS THE FAMOUS KATINA?

THERE WERE MOMENTS OF LEVITY, such as when Ntinos, the self-appointed village jester, staged a mock court among the prosecution witnesses while they waited their turn to be called to testify. Ntinos stood his ground while in the witness stand, and later had fun with Panaitakis, whose fascination with the unique tidal phenomenon of Halkida's waters and the mystery around it earned a gentle mocking.

Thanasis was grateful for Ntinos's comic relief. The witnesses had been cooped up for days, confined by the trial for hours at a stretch. When the defense tried to fool the prosecution witnesses into thinking that the food was somehow better at their hotel than it was at the prosecution's hotel, Thanasis's team spread a counter-rumor about huge platters of special white fish, expensive local white wine, and more homemade cakes that could be eaten at their hotel.

Amidst all this, Thanasis had yet to find out word about George Nitsos's prior conviction in his youth. Thanasis's attorneys had informed him that the court records had been found and were now in Athens, but had they been sent yet? Even with the attorney general on his side, Thanasis knew delays could occur.

On Friday, March 18, Thanasis took a seat alongside the prosecution and did a double-take at the size of the gathering crowd. There were people stuffed into the courtroom, the hallways, and the grounds outside, where they overflowed down the steps onto the street.

They were all there to see Katina, the now infamous young adulteress, whom many blamed for Panayota's murder. Immaculately dressed, she sat in the front row, her eyes cast downward.

"So this is the famous Katina?" someone behind Thanasis whispered.

"Is this the woman the terrible murder took place for?" someone else asked.

All eyes were trained unmercifully on the young woman, but when it came time for her to take the witness stand, the courtroom was cleared, so the public would not hear matters that would surely cause them moral outrage.

When she left the courtroom that evening, she was greeted by flashbulbs by the newspaper photographers. A crowd had gathered on the steps, the men among them staring hungrily at her. Her exit, along with her teary testimony, was described in the newspapers the next day. The *Acropolis* called her "the enigmatic young lover of Nitsos" and pointed out that throughout her testimony she was "shaking with sobs."

The reporter, editorializing, wondered if she was sacrificing herself for George. The papers also made sure to mention Katina's last tryst with George, calling it an "orgy" at the altar of the village's church.

Zanias, Katina's cousin, took the witness stand the next morning and repeated much of his testimony from Athens. George, he claimed, had pressured Katina into having a relationship with him and had threatened her with dire consequences should she resist his romantic overtures.

"Katina told me," Zanias said, "that Nitsos had taken her virginity. In the beginning, they had just been enjoying themselves. But later he promised to marry her after divorcing Panayota.

"Her father was a weak man," he added. "She had been in charge of her own life. I felt I needed to intervene and protect her from dragging herself deeper into the mud. I wanted to protect the family's name from becoming sullied."

When Katina was called again to the witness stand, she said that Zanias had hit her because she didn't want to go back to her parents.

"Did you tell him about losing your virginity to Nitsos?" the prosecution asked.

"Why would I want to talk about my virginity with my cousin?" she shot back. She paused a moment before adding, "One day he pulled me down onto my bed and tried to kiss me, but I managed to break free."

Zanias joined the cross-examination, asking her several questions, but that only angered her.

"You're a shameless man!" she shouted at him.

"*You* calling *me* shameless?" Zanias snapped. "It's you who has brought shame to your house and become a mere puppet in that Linatsas's hands. You're nothing but an unscrupulous slut."

He stood up, marched to the stand angrily, and spat on his cousin.

CHAPTER 45:
"JUST ONE DAY"

ON THE FOLLOWING MONDAY, MARCH 21, Basil was called to the witness stand. Tall, upright, and bespectacled, the attorney and notary was far and away the most educated of the witnesses. He wore his hair combed back and spoke slowly and deliberately, evincing an unmistakable air of sophistication.

"George Nitsos is disrespectful and crude," he said when asked about the accused. "He doesn't even spare young schoolgirls from his vulgar humor, and he flaunts his wealth and power in the village."

Thanasis, seated with the prosecution, recalled the night of the murder. Had it not been for Basil's wise counsel, he might have taken justice into his own hands that night and gone after George.

Basil had avoided the witness stand during the first trial, but now it appeared he was determined to make amends. He spoke confidently and forthrightly.

"I was asleep when the guns were fired," he explained, "and I didn't hear them. Then from my balcony I saw the lights at the Gumases', and I heard Nitsos saying, 'Who has killed her? Who?' And I hurried there."

"What was going on there?" the prosecution asked.

"The people were trying to help Panayota, and I myself urged Thanasis Konandreas to go and call for the doctor."

"Did Konandreas tell you that Nitsos was behind the shooting?"

"Yes. He told me in private that Nitsos had done it, and when I asked whether he thought Nitsos himself had done it, he said, 'No, he asked someone else.' Konandreas was really upset and said, 'I'm going to kill the bastard. I'm going to go home, get my pistol, and blow his brains into the air.' He was determined to kill him, and I calmed him down by telling him about his family obligations and the need to do

231

other things at that moment. I told him to make his report when the police arrived."

"Did you speak to Nitsos at all?"

"Nitsos seemed indifferent to what was happening around him, and because of what Konandreas had told me and what I myself thought, I didn't try to console him."

"Were Konandreas's words so convincing?"

"His words made me think and when combined with Nitsos's behavior, which disturbed me, began to make sense. He was doing nothing to help. This made no sense to me so I was compelled to believe Konandreas's words."

"Did Nitsos himself have anything to say about this?"

"He approached me the next day and said that the victim's dying words were, 'Vasilios has killed us.'"

"Did you hear Konandreas telling Panayota, 'Vasilios didn't kill you; I told you who would'?"

"No, I didn't, but others did and spoke about it later."

"Could it be that they were trying to kill Nitsos and in error they shot Panayota?"

"The killer shot the one he wanted," Basil answered, "and the fact that he shot from behind the small pear tree, which was ahead of, and not behind the walking couple, means that he wasn't afraid of being seen."

"Did you not think that anyone else besides Nitsos could have committed the crime?"

"Konandreas's name certainly didn't cross my mind, though the police asked me if I suspected him. Konandreas loved his cousin, and even if he wanted to kill Nitsos, he would never have attempted anything that could have put Panayota's life at risk. And the actual shooting that happened did more than put her life at risk. I also don't believe the theory that Konandreas wanted to take over the village store as sole proprietor. Nitsos was an asset to their business. I saw Konandreas at the store until closing time on the night of the murder. The defense attacks and accuses him and wants to neutralize him because he is the main witness for the prosecution."

Basil paused a moment before running through the list of potential suspects. "The owner of the other store in the village," he said. "It is inconceivable that he committed this murder out of business rivalry. He's peaceful and wouldn't have the heart to kill even a bird.

"Vasilios is a good man. He does his job and minds his own

business. He wouldn't stoop low enough to kill because of a petty rivalry. If Nitsos was convinced that Panayota was shot by him, he should have gone after him and reported him to the police.

"Zanias could have done it in revenge for the dishonor Nitsos brought the family by sullying his cousin Katina, but it has been confirmed that Zanias was in Athens at the time of the murder. He has no one in Kupaki who would murder someone for him. So Zanias has to be ruled out.

"So that leaves Nitsos. I believe he asked Karaiskos to kill Panayota. The entire area around the village says that the accused are guilty."

"Were you present when the test firing to find the killer's gun was carried out?" asked the defense.

"Yes," Basil answered. "I saw the captain pick up the shell from the crime scene, and since that time, I have never seen that shell again I don't believe that the captain, who is a very good and sincere man, made a mistake and mixed up the shells."

"Could someone else have dropped a shell from Karaiskos's gun at the crime scene to incriminate him?"

"I don't believe that would have been possible."

The defense attorney stroked his chin thoughtfully. "You said that Nitsos was doing nothing to help when his wife was shot, and that made you wonder if he was culpable in some way."

"That's correct."

"Did it not occur to you that this apathy could have been caused by shock?"

"I don't believe so. In any case, in Kupaki we call this sort of apathy cowardice."

"And in Kupaki, does cowardice make a man a murderer?"

When Basil didn't answer, the defense attorney raised the issue of Thanasis's last words to Panayota. "Thanasis said, 'Vasilios didn't kill you; I told you who would.' Was it not inhuman?"

"It was an expression of indignation," Basil shot back.

"Why did Konandreas, who you consider trustworthy, not tell you anything about Nitsos asking different people to kill his wife?"

"He didn't want to give publicity to such a private family matter," Basil answered.

The defense moved on to Thanasis's criminal past, bringing up the time he had beaten a man in the village.

"That incident has now been forgotten in the village," Basil said. "Today Konandreas is an exemplary family man."

"You saw Nitsos's thigh wound from the gunshot," the defense attorney said, changing directions once again. "How close was this to his genitals?"

"Perhaps about eight inches away," Basil answered. "For as good of a shooter as Karaiskos is, that's safe."

"What kind of man was Karaiskos?"

"He was a poor and good man."

The defense attorney zeroed in on the comment. "And you believe that such a good man, as you yourself call him, is capable of murder?"

"Nitsos is capable of murder and more," Basil retorted. "And he has, I'm sure, used a lot of persuasion and perhaps many threats to make Karaiskos commit the crime. I did say that Karaiskos was good, but I also said that he was poor. It was this poverty that Nitsos exploited to his advantage."

Polyxeni returned home from Halkida on March 20th, and before she could address any of her children's concerns, Grandma Efthemia emerged from the house with her own list of questions. She wanted to know about Father's health, his state of mind, and of course the trial.

My brothers and I noticed a roll of newspapers in her bag, and soon I was reading aloud from the last few editions of the *Ethnos*, which covered in detail the incident in court when the defense had accused Father of being the murderer and gave a blow-by-blow account of the examinations of Mother and several other people from the village.

"Will they be convicted?" Grandma asked.

"I don't know," Mother answered honestly. "But everyone says this is a better court altogether."

"What does Thanasis think?" Grandma pressed.

"He also thinks this is a better court."

Soon Mitros appeared on the porch. "Welcome, Xeni," he said, giving Mother a hug.

"How are you, Uncle?"

Mitros ignored Polyxeni's question and launched into his favorite topic. "How do the jurors look?" He studied her intently, as though he feared taking his eyes off her, afraid that she might vanish before he got his answers.

Mother recapped the facts and then added, "I just want them to get one day. Just one day in jail as guilty men will do. I don't want them to come back free."

Our teacher learned that Mother was back, and during our lunch break the next day, he showed up on our front porch to ask for newspapers. "Welcome back to Kupaki, Polyxeni," he said heartily. "How did it go?"

"Like the crab, Teacher, like the crab," Mother replied, using the Greek metaphor for a slow and difficult process.

"I think it's going in the right direction, though," the teacher said. "The judge and the prosecutor seem to have more control than they had in Athens."

Mitros appeared at his window, having heard the conversation. "The verdict comes from the jury, Teacher, not from the judge or the prosecutor!" he shouted, startling the teacher, who nearly cricked his neck turning around in bewilderment.

"I see ten years, old man," the teacher said after regaining his composure and grinning at Mitros.

"I say twenty," Mitros responded, not to be outdone.

Mother muttered under her breath as Mitros and the teacher threw numbers back and forth. "Ten years! Twenty years!" she grumbled. "All I want is just one day."

"All right, old man, you're on," the teacher said, accepting Mitros's bet. "If they get more than ten years, I will lose a hundred drachmas to you. Now what about you?"

Mitros pointed toward his favorite beehive at the end of a long row of them. "All the honey from that one in the corner."

The hive was the old man's pride and joy, which meant he was feeling awfully confident about the bet. He and the teacher had worked on it together, so the teacher, too, had to know it was a bigger honey producer.

"Fifteen is a tie," Mitros concluded.

CHAPTER 46:
SURPRISE

THANASIS WAS SEATED BESIDE THE prosecution team on March 22 when his sister Aggelo approached the witness stand.

"I was at the Kumes party when the shots were fired," she told the court. "I was waiting to take my children home. After the shots were fired, I went to the Gumases', where Panayota had been taken."

"Did you hear Panayota say anything?"

"I heard her asking Thanasis, 'Do you think Vasilios has killed us?' And he replied, 'No, Vasilios didn't kill you. I told you who would.' And then Basil was telling Thanasis, 'Thanasis, we have other things to do now—getting a doctor, getting to a telephone quickly. This is not the time to talk about killing.' I could see that Thanasis was really upset."

"Did Panayota say anything else to you?"

"She told me that she wanted to see her mother. Following that, Nitsos's sister, Alexandra, who was beside Panayota, consoling her, said, 'Be patient, my bird. The doctor is on his way, and he'll make you better quickly. And when you get well, we shall take you with us to our house.' And Panayota, as she was dying, told Alexandra, 'Now that you have devoured me...' Then Vasilios arrived, and because I had heard people saying things about him, I regarded him with suspicion, but he was looking sad and was also doing a lot to help Panayota."

"What was Nitsos doing?"

"He was silent and impassive. In fact, the entire village cried for Panayota that night except her husband."

"What are you implying Nitsos should have done?"

"I'm a woman who has lost her husband," Aggelo answered. "When he died, I felt my whole world was going to pieces, and I expressed it,

236

but when his wife lay dying, Nitsos was behaving as though nothing untoward had happened."

"How were the Nitsoses getting along?" Judge Demopoulos asked. "Was Nitsos treating your cousin well?"

"*Well?* What well! He was trying to kill her for eleven years, Judge!"

The crowd burst into laughter, and Papandreou, taking advantage of the interruption and without any objection from the judge, launched into a recitation of the many people George had asked, directly or indirectly, to kill Panayota: "Panaitakis and Mary, and Sakis and... Harry." The list was a long one.

Finally the judge resumed with his questions. "Did Panayota ever complain to you about her husband, or mention that she knew that he had plans to kill her?"

"No. Panayota loved him. Besides, I was one of the people who had told her not to marry him, so she would not have complained to me, because she would have felt that I would say, 'I told you so,' and leave her to her suffering. Of course, I would never have said nor done anything like that, but Panayota didn't know that. I did find out from others about Nitsos's plans to kill her, though. And I used to tell her to leave him, but she would say, 'I'm not going to let another woman take my place in this house,' and I could see how distressed she was."

"Did Panayota visit you during the afternoon the day she was killed?"

"Yes, she did."

"Did she mention anything about any plans to be at the Zakkases' later?"

"Before she left my place, she said, 'I'm going to spend a little time at the Zakkases' place.' But she didn't say, 'I'm going to the Zakkases' for dinner tonight,' as far as I can remember."

During the recess that followed, Thanasis was surprised to see George Nitsos's family from America enter the courtroom. Reporters reached for their cameras, while onlookers buzzed with excitement.

The older Nitsos, graying at the temples and tottering unsteadily toward his son, wrapped George in a tender embrace.

But the public prosecutor, apparently unmoved by the unfolding scene, scolded the policemen standing nearby. "What are you here for?" he asked sternly. "Are you standing guard for a theater production?"

The policemen dutifully broke up the hug and then ushered George into another room, where he would spend the rest of the recess in isolation.

"Yes, I'm quite sure I heard it," twenty-year-old Effie said from the witness stand. "Alexandra did say, 'Be patient, my darling, until the doctor comes. When you get well, I'll take you with me to my house.' And Panayota answered in a very feeble voice, because she had no strength left."

"And what did Panayota say?" the prosecution asked.

"She said, 'You have devoured me.' And even though I couldn't understand what she meant by it, I knew at the time that Panayota knew who was behind the shooting."

"Did you know of the relationship between Nitsos and Katina?"

Effie nodded. "I saw them kissing inside Nitsos's store only days before the murder. After the murder, I told Katina that she had made a mistake in having a relationship with an older, married man, and she replied that it was an honor that Nitsos killed his wife because of her."

Palos then asked Effie several questions about dating at the village and how young people managed to do it.

Judge Demopoulos interrupted the attorney. "These questions aren't pertinent to the case, Counsel," he said. "The case is not about village gossip but about the murder of a woman."

"That seems to be a biased comment, Your Honor, which seems to originate from the anxiety that the witness's answers may be favorable to the accused."

"That's a direct accusation leveled against the bench, Counsel," the judge snapped. "I ask you to retract your statement."

"I stand by my statement," Palos countered.

Kumes, the young man who had asked George if he could borrow his gramophone on the night of the murder, was the next to take the witness stand.

"Did you meet Socrates Karaiskos on the day after the murder?" the defense asked.

"Yes, shortly before noon," Kumes replied.

"Did Karaiskos say anything about the murder at all?"

"He asked me whom I suspected, and I replied that I didn't know. He then said that he suspected Vasilios and the father of Poly. He seemed sure that one of the two was the murderer."

"What did you say in response to that?"

"I said that it couldn't be Poly's father, since he was in Athens at the time."

"Do you think the gun shell from the crime scene was possibly mixed with the test-fired ones?"

"No, I don't."

"Was Karaiskos's gun bad?"

"I'm a hunter myself," Kumes answered, "and hunting partner of Karaiskos. His gun was good enough to murder the woman."

"You said you're a hunter. Do you keep the feathers on the game for as long as Karaiskos did?"

"No, we remove the feathers and eat the game right away. What Karaiskos did with the bird I find suspicious."

The most shocking revelation came when Proedros, a defense witness, recently elected president of the village council, contradicted his prior testimonies. The court decided to press charges, accusing him of perjury, and the fifty-one-year-old man ended up in custody. He was found guilty of perjury later.

The next day, March 25th, Greek Independence Day, when I reached the newspaper shop at Krokylion, all the papers had sold out. Flustered and out of breath, I lingered indecisively. The idea of returning home empty-handed was too embarrassing to contemplate.

Just then, Father Kritsas, the local priest, appeared like an angel. He was a close friend of Papazois, and I had served next to him as an altar boy during joint services on big holidays. *"Papuli,"* I said, addressing him as my grandfather, "can you help me get a newspaper?"

Father Kritsas, standing erect and towering above me, gazed down at me bemusedly. "The shop owner has newspapers, my boy. I only have the Gospels." A smile creased his face. "Anyway, who are you?"

"Papuli, I'm Lukas Konandreas, Thanasis Konandreas's son," I said quickly, "and they sent me from Kupaki for the *Ethnos.*"

"Thanasis's son, eh?" Father Kritsas said, suddenly regarding me with fresh interest.

"And Papazois's nephew, *Papuli,"* I added hopefully.

"Papazois? He was at the court, wasn't he? Has he returned?"

"Yes, he's in Kupaki now, *Papuli.*"

The priest stood thinking a moment. Then he shouted to the shopkeeper in a booming voice, "How are we going to find an *Ethnos* for this boy to take to Kupaki?"

"All the papers are sold out, *Papuli,*" the shopkeeper replied.

"Stay here," Father Kritsas said. "Let me see what I can do."

The priest marched purposefully through the crowd, toward a section of the village where I knew no newspaper stores were located. A few minutes later he reappeared with a newspaper tucked under his arm.

"*Efcharisto, Papuli!*" I said, gratefully accepting the newspaper.

"God bless you, my son," he said and waved away my hand when I offered him the coins I'd carried with me.

Fleet of foot and light of heart, I rushed back to Kupaki, mission accomplished.

CHAPTER 47:
THINK OF YOUR CHILD

THE NEXT DAY, WHEN THE court broke for lunch, Thanasis took the public prosecutor aside. "Mr. Papandreou," he said quietly, "has the paper about Nitsos's prior conviction come from Athens yet?"

"No, I'm afraid not," Papandreou answered. "But don't worry. We don't need it just yet. I know they have it in Athens, and it will be with us when we need it."

"There's another thing, Mr. Papandreou…"

"Yes?"

Thanasis had been ruminating over something George Nitsos had said during the first trial. "During the trial in Athens, Nitsos claimed that he was playing a game called *Koumkan* at the Zakkases' on the night of the murder, didn't he?"

"Yes," Papandreou said after mulling over the question.

"Well, I've been thinking about it. I don't think Nitsos knows how to play that game, unless he has learned it recently in prison. He certainly never played it in Kupaki from what I remember."

"Hmm," Papandreou said, rubbing his chin. "I see what you're getting at. It's definitely worth a try, even if it only makes the jury feel that Nitsos is a habitual liar and can't be trusted. But one thing baffles me: if Nitsos doesn't know how to play *Koumkan*, why didn't he name a game he knows?"

"I know how that liar's mind works," Thanasis answered. "He's too cocksure to believe he could get caught in a lie. He just had to impress the crowd. Nothing mundane will do for George Nitsos, so if he lies about playing a game, he would lie that he played a game that sounds grand—like *Koumkan*."

Next on the witness stand that afternoon was Socrates Karaiskos. The prosecution team managed to have George taken away to another room during Socrates's testimony, arguing that George often interrupted the witnesses and showed total contempt for court procedure. Socrates was more likely to give uninhibited testimony, the prosecution argued, if George wasn't present.

"Gentlemen of the jury," Socrates said at the first chance he got to speak, "I have been accused of killing a woman who was like a mother and a sister to me—the wife of my best man. I'm innocent. Konandreas has set me up."

"So are you convinced that someone other than Nitsos was behind the murder?" Judge Demopoulos asked.

"I am. Nitsos and his wife were living happily together. He had no reason to do it."

"How do you support yourself and pay your legal fees now that you're in jail? Does Nitsos help?"

"My brothers-in-law help me," Socrates answered, "not Nitsos."

"Have you and Nitsos ever gone hunting together?"

"We used to, before he injured his leg."

"Were you his confidant?"

"All the people I work for trust me and take me into their confidence."

"Were you Nitsos's protégé when he was the commander of his band?"

"No."

"Has he ever been displeased with you?"

"No."

"Have you ever argued?"

"I never get into arguments."

"On the night of the murder, Nitsos had a party. Why did he not invite you, his best man?"

"I don't move in his circles. I'm not a very important person in our community, but Nitsos is."

"Did Nitsos tell you about any marital problems?"

"Never."

"Has he ever confessed to you about his affair with Katina?"

"Never."

"Have you ever felt unable to say no to Nitsos?"

"No."

"Is Nitsos a persuasive man?"

Socrates shrugged. "I don't know. I've never felt that."

"When you and he used to go hunting, had you ever been on the path where the murder later took place?"

"We've been on all the village paths."

"Has it been a long time since you were last on that path?"

"I don't remember."

"Have you ever climbed up the ravine toward the hill at the place where the shots were fired at the Nitsoses?"

"Never."

"Were you convinced, as people have testified, that in 1946 Nitsos wanted to kill his wife?"

"No," Socrates answered adamantly, "and I don't believe that story. It's a lie."

"Karaiskos, you've heard the witnesses. You've heard Basil. You've heard the state police major. Why do you think Basil and the major say and believe things about you which you deny?"

"How should I know? I'm not inside Basil's head, but he's a good man, and he doesn't lie. He probably believes what he's saying because he's been misled by Konandreas. As for the major, it's his job to not completely believe things he hears during his interrogations."

"Do you think about your child, Karaiskos? How long has it been since you held her in your arms?"

"A whole year."

The judge sighed deeply. "Look here, Karaiskos," he said slowly and deliberately, "Nitsos is not here. He was sent away from the courtroom in order to let you speak freely. I'm addressing your intellect, not your emotions, so as to make you think with a cool head about your wife and your daughter. If by any chance you're involved in this murder but have promised to keep quiet, I want you to know that you're not bound by any other contract here. You stand here before Greek justice. A woman you consider equal to a mother or a sister asks for justice from her grave. So tell the court the truth and nothing but the truth. Did anyone brainwash you to commit the murder?"

"Nobody has brainwashed me," Socrates insisted. "I have told you all I know."

"When your wife told you that Panayota named Vasilios as the murderer, what did you think?"

"I thought it was possible, because Nitsos and Vasilios had problems with each other." Socrates paused before adding, "The police beat me with a wire cable for three hours to make me sign a false confession."

"If that was the case, why did none of the villagers hear anything from the school?"

"I'm not the kind of person to scream and weep," Socrates answered. "That doesn't mean that it didn't hurt."

"Why didn't you mention this mistreatment during your initial testimony?"

"I didn't have the experience to know that I could complain."

The public prosecutor took over the questioning. "Why hadn't you eaten the partridge that you claim you shot on the day of the murder? Why did you have it ready to show as proof that your gun was fired on it and not on Panayota?"

"I didn't have salt to cook it with," Socrates explained, "so I kept it with me until I got home."

"Then why didn't you give it to your wife to cook when you got home?"

"I forgot about it, with the news of the murder. I remembered about it only when the captain arrived later. That's why it had the feathers on it still. Besides, it didn't smell."

"You claim that you lit a fire on the hill on which you spent the night with your sheep. Did you light it as an alibi?"

"No, I did it to keep the mosquitoes off me and the jackals off my lambs. Only people who have to sleep rough in the open know about these things."

"If you don't know what Nitsos was doing on Sunday, how can you say he's not guilty?"

"He's not!"

"Can you rule out the possibility that Nitsos did it for Katina?"

"Yes, I can."

"How did Nitsos's callous conduct appear to you after the murder?"

"I wasn't there to see it. I only heard about it, and I'm not sure people are telling the truth."

"Why didn't you bring as witnesses those who told you to hide your gun on that Monday morning when you were on your way to the village?"

"I didn't have the money to bring them here."

"How do we know that you didn't hide the gun the night before the murder?"

"I hid it in the morning."

"Did Nitsos tell you what sort of gun his wife had been shot with?"

"No."

March drew to a close, and the swallows returned to Kupaki to inspect their mud nests. The snow, meanwhile, had retreated to the surrounding mountaintops. Spring was everywhere: every bud on every tree, bush, and flower looked ready to burst.

For those in the village, however, life had come to a standstill. The village church walls had been closed since the previous autumn, when interior work had begun. And gardens remained untilled since half the villagers were away at court and the other half were insatiably gobbling up news of the trial in their spare moments.

And Polyxeni's anxieties and fears were undiminished even when reports and editorials coming from newspapers known to be friendly to Nitsos were predicting that the accused would be found guilty. She was repeating the "Just one day."

CHAPTER 48:
"ARE YOU NOT
GEORGE NITSOS?"

As GEORGE NITSOS WAS CALLED to the witness stand on Friday, March 31, Thanasis spotted Papandreou, the public prosecutor, carving his way toward him through the thick crowd of people.

"Konandreas! I have it right here!" the public prosecutor said jubilantly, tapping the inside pocket of his jacket.

A relieved Thanasis smiled back and then turned his attention to the front of the court.

"The court will read the testimony of Socrates Karaiskos now," Judge Demopoulos announced, "since George Nitsos was absent during it."

"I'm not interested in what Karaiskos said," Nitsos said flatly.

"But I am," the judge said, "because that's what the law dictates."

After Socrates's testimony had been read in its entirety, George addressed the court. "I'm very saddened that I've been accused of being a wife killer," he said and went on to retell the story of how he had met and married Panayota. He then described the day of the murder and what had happened in the days that followed it.

"It's all Konandreas's doing," he said. "He's the one who's really guilty of this murder, and he's trying to frame me. Vasilios and all those other people who make up stories that Konandreas likes to hear, stories about my plans to kill my wife, are assassinating my character.

"I have never denied in court anything that is true—like my relationship with Katina. There are many such women among us. Nobody thinks of marrying a woman like that, much less killing one's wife for her. I may have strayed, but I never left my wife. I'm not proud of my extramarital relationship, but I'm sure I'm not the only sinner in this room in that regard. Try me here as an adulterer, and I'll plead guilty. But I'm being tried as a murderer, and I plead not guilty, because I'm completely innocent of that charge. I ask you to acquit me, and I'll deliver justice the true murderers of my wife."

"If you know who the murderers are," the judge said, "why don't you name them here now?"

"Because my hands are tied. I'm behind bars, and Konandreas is free. The villagers, who fear a 'guilty' verdict, hesitate to say anything against Konandreas. If I'm convicted, they're at his mercy in Kupaki. He's a powerful man there, now that he has taken over the store and livestock and other assets that we jointly owned."

Thanasis shook his head dismissively but otherwise kept his poise.

"Why did your sister, Eleni, after the card game, not go with you and your wife on the night of the murder to sleep at your place? She used to do that almost every night, didn't she?"

"Eleni had slept at the Zakkases' three other nights before the night of the murder," George answered. "On that night, when I left with Panayota, I did ask Eleni to come with us, but she said that she had to do her laundry the next day at the Zakkases'."

"When you were shot, were you not able to see anything? You had a flashlight, did you not? Did you not even see the shadow of the man who shot you?"

"No, I didn't."

"Did you hear the footsteps of the killer leaving?"

"No."

"Why didn't you pick your wife up from where she had fallen? Why did Gumas have to do it?"

"I was limping because of my injuries, and in my confused mental state at the time, it just didn't occur to me."

"When did your wife say, 'Vasilios has killed us'?"

"While she was being carried to the Gumases' house."

"What did you tell her when she said that?"

"I told her not to worry and promised her I would find the shooter."

"Why didn't you ask her if she had seen Vasilios?"

"I just didn't."

"I insist: why not?"

"It simply didn't occur to me to ask."

"Did your wife repeat what she had said about Vasilios?"

"Yes, in the Gumases' yard."

"Did you ask her this second time if she had seen him?"

"I didn't, but if I had known then that things would come to this point, I would have."

"I'm compelled to conclude from your answers that you had no excuse not to ask your wife more about her suspicions about Vasilios," the judge said. "And why did you not mobilize the men carrying guns in the village?"

"Not even two divisions of the army would have been able to find and arrest the killer because of the forest," George replied. "Anyway, before my wife died, I did call for the police."

"Why didn't you chase the killer yourself?"

"I couldn't do that without a gun."

"Did the killer know that you had no gun?"

"The killer seemed more than sure that I didn't," George answered. "Because of the trauma, I have no memory of moving away from my wife, or of Panayota being moved to the Gumases', or of the care some women gave me later, or of the moment Panayota died, or of Vasilios being there in the Gumases' yard. Konandreas was trying to kill me, not Panayota. I began suspecting this from the day after the murder because he didn't come and ask me what had happened as other people in the village had done. I heard from others that Konandreas told my wife that Vasilios was not the killer and that he had told her who would kill her. I'm sure Konandreas had prepared this phrase to use it at a time like that, so that any suspicion about Vasilios could be diverted."

"Did your wife know of your relationships with other women?"

"No. She trusted me. Even when that Marula woman told her that her Goddaughter had seen me and Katina kissing, Panayota did not believe it and argued for me against all the gossipmongers."

"Did you not force Katina into the relationship with threats?"

"Certainly not. She knew exactly what she was doing. Contrary to what has been said here, she was no virgin when she slept with me. She never asked me what would happen to her, and I never promised to marry her."

"Did you tell her three hours before the murder that she should not talk even if someone took her teeth out?"

"Yes, but that had nothing to do with the murder. I meant that she shouldn't talk about our relationship. There were plenty of rumors circulating already."

"Are you aware that Basil has also testified here against you?"

"Well, what do you expect with Konandreas breathing down his neck?" George shot back. "This's exactly what I said about Konandreas's authority in the village."

George Nitsos was on the stand again on Friday, April 1. This time Papandreou, the public prosecutor, was asking the questions.

"If you suspected Konandreas, as you have told the court earlier," Papandreou began, "why didn't you apprehend him with your suspicions? Have you spoken to him since the night of the murder?"

"No, I didn't apprehend him or speak to him after the murder," George answered, "but I did tell the police and my attorneys about my suspicions."

"Immediately after the shooting, did you think your wife was going to die, or were you hopeful about saving her life?"

"I thought she was going to live."

"Since you hoped that she would live, what did you do to save her?"

"I sent my brother-in-law Zakkas to bring a doctor."

"Why didn't you grab Konandreas and tell him, 'Thanasis, my friend, my relative, my partner'—whatever you liked to call him—'run for a doctor,' since you knew he owned a horse and Zakkas didn't?"

"I had no need for Konandreas. I sent my brother-in-law, who had more sympathy for my wife than Konandreas did."

"And what did you feel about your wife's plight?"

"I was anxious, of course. I loved her." George spoke in a reverent tone. "I still do."

"What did you do that night out of love for your wife? Did you not move away and lie down on a blanket as your wife was fighting for her life?"

"I didn't know that I was expected to act theatrically and demonstrate my love for my wife for all to see."

"Is someone who cries and brings the world down when his wife's life is in danger an actor?"

"I was taking care of my wife," George insisted, "and I had no desire to talk unnecessarily."

"When you recovered your senses at the Gumas household, did you express your intense pain to ask who had killed your wife? Would that not have been natural?"

"I was waiting for the police."

"When the police came, what did you tell them? Did you tell them, 'Vasilios killed her'? Those three words. Did you help them in any way to find your wife's killer?"

"I told them what my wife had said."

"From the time the gun was fired until the time your wife died from her wounds, you had nothing to say. Why were your lips sealed?"

"I told you: I was expecting the police."

"We know where you were that night. But do you know how Karaiskos can prove his whereabouts?"

"You know he was in the countryside with his lambs," George replied.

Papandreou kept hammering away. "When you saw Karaiskos the next day, did you tell him, 'Come here, Karaiskos. They accuse you as the killer'?"

"No."

"Did you not say that Konandreas was once accused of being a rustler?"

"Yes, he was. A higher court later dropped the case against him."

"Why does Konandreas refer to you as Linatsas?"

"It's a nickname from my childhood that Konandreas spread around."

"Have you ever been found guilty in court, and if so, why?"

Thanasis, watching from the front row, tried to suppress his excitement. Papandreou was finally going after George's record.

"Yes," George answered. "For embezzling some money from the church."

"Were you ever accused of anything during your time at Patras?"

"I can't remember. I think it was something about a broken bicycle twenty-five years ago. That's a long time ago."

"You have called Konandreas a rustler, though he was only accused and never convicted about twenty-five years ago."

"Is a bicycle incident the same as rustling, Mr. Prosecutor?"

"Mr. Nitsos, I have here a verdict that shows you were found guilty of rustling."

"I was never accused of rustling."

Papandreou removed the papers from the inside pocket of his jacket, his eyes dancing. "I would like to submit a certified copy of the decision of the penal court of Patras, number 1703, dated May 11, 1934, along with the court records pertaining to this case."

Gunaris rose to his feet for the defense. "Has this been submitted as part of the prosecution's records for this trial?"

"If there is an objection, I should like to hear it first," Judge Demopoulos said. "Then the court shall rule."

"This submission is unacceptable," Gunaris argued, "and against court procedure."

"The submission of documents is allowed until the end of the proceedings in any court," Papandreou countered. "Surely the defense attorney is aware of that."

"I object, Your Honor." This time it was Palos who was on his feet. "Such submissions have to be done before the testimony of the accused. That has always been the procedure."

"The rules are clear on this matter," Papandreou retorted. "A submission of this kind can be made right up to the end of the testimony of the accused. The accused here has not completed his testimony."

The prosecution attorneys then supported the public prosecutor, and the court accepted the submission of the certificate by Papandreou.

Just before two p.m., the court adjourned for three hours, during which time the papers submitted by the prosecutor created a huge upheaval in the chambers.

Papandreou winked at Thanasis on his way out of the courtroom, and his cheerfulness was infectious. Thanasis found his own spirits lifting.

At five p.m., after the hearing resumed, Papandreou went in for the kill.

"Nitsos," he said, making no effort to hide his exuberance, "you were accused of rustling and found guilty of stealing a lamb, were you not?"

"I don't know anything about this. This must be someone else."

"Are you not George Nitsos, son of Ioannes and Maria Nitsos, as the verdict here says?"

"No. I mean, yes, I am. But this is not about me. It must be synonymy."

"Listen, Nitsos, you have denied everything spoken against you here, and you have told us that all of the prosecution witnesses have lied. Are you now denying official papers? Now tell me how the game of *Koumkan* is played."

Thanasis shook his head in wonderment. Papandreou was plying things perfectly.

"The game of what?" George asked, clearly thrown by the question.

"*Koumkan*. Was that not the game you said you were playing at the Zakkases' on the night of the murder?"

"Give me a deck of cards," George said, slowly regaining his usual confidence, "and I'll show you."

"Please describe the game for me in words."

"I cannot. Give me a deck, and I'll show you."

Judge Demopoulos, who no doubt had seen attorneys trap witnesses in numerous ways, was now staring at the public prosecutor with undisguised surprise, his mouth hanging slightly open in a most un-judgelike manner.

"Does anyone have a deck of cards?" Papandreou's voice boomed with newfound authority. "Your Honor, I have to insist on continuing this line of questioning."

The public prosecutor then returned his attention to George. "Nitsos, how is *Koumkan* played? What do the players do once the hands are dealt?"

"I'm not a card player," George said. "I've only played this game a few times, and I can't remember it now."

"Try to remember how you played it on the night of the murder. Or did you not play cards?"

"Why are you browbeating me like this?" George asked, clearly on the defensive now. "Why don't you just go ahead and make your own judgment?"

"Very well then. I will. Nitsos, you were not playing *Koumkan*. You were indifferent and cold, keeping the game going until eleven p.m., the time Socrates Karaiskos would be ready at a previously agreed upon hiding place to shoot and kill your wife."

The silence in the courtroom could only mean one thing, Thanasis thought. Papandreou had pulled it off. The jury was on their side.

CHAPTER 49:
NO PUNISHMENT TOO HARSH

THE NEXT DAY, APRIL 2, Papandreou stood before the court. Dressed in a dark suit, with a white shirt and black tie, he stroked his thin mustache absentmindedly while preparing to deliver his closing remarks.

Thanasis, seated behind the two defendants, looked on earnestly. He had done all he could. The case would soon be in the hands of the jury.

"Gentlemen of the jury," the public prosecutor began, "I will not limit myself to discussing whether the accused are guilty or not, because it's not so important to add a couple more names to the ledger of convicted criminals. What is of interest, however, is the injury inflicted on Greek justice at the trial in Athens, where George Nitsos was portrayed as an innocent man, despite all the evidence from the crime scene and the behavior of Nitsos after the crime, which has established his guilt beyond doubt.

"During the long deliberations, the honorable judge agonized over every piece of evidence and every seemingly useless detail, each of which you have to decide to accept or reject. Why do we need all this agony, effort, and fatigue? To ensure that you have every piece of information that will help you make an informed decision. For Greek justice is all about knowledge dispelling ignorance, light dispelling darkness. For me personally, all this evidence was unnecessary in the light of two significant sources of information: the murder weapon and the testimony of Nitsos himself.

"Nitsos's testimony is enough to convince even his own father, if that gentleman still believes his son is innocent of killing his wife. Let's just look at the crime scene as the ordinary villagers of Kupaki would. The accused is the only eyewitness of the murder. The first question toward the only eyewitness would be: 'Nitsos, what exactly happened at that moment?' 'Nothing,' he replies. 'Did you hear anything? Did you see anyone?' 'No,' he answers with a shrug. 'Did you think about fighting back?' 'No.'

"Would you not say that this is highly suspicious? We simply cannot exclude the possibility that he knows the killer and doesn't want to name him."

As Papandreou spoke, George and Socrates listened impassively, although George occasionally jotted down notes or whispered to Ms. Mazarakis, one of the defense attorneys.

"Now take the testimonies of the witnesses," Papandreou continued. "Whom would you have first? Zakkas? What did he tell us? They heard the first shot, and they rushed outside and screamed and shouted, but nobody answered them. They then heard a second shot and then heard the words, 'They have killed us.' And Zakkas explained that Nitsos told them, 'Nothing has happened to me. Take care of my wife.'

"A village has been turned upside down. Nitsos is unconcerned. Nitsos is questioned. He gives no answer. The whole of Kupaki rushes about. Nitsos takes no action. Oh, yes... he did ask for coffee!

"We have more questions: 'What happened after the death of your wife? Who carried your wife away to safety?' Nitsos ignores everything. Nitsos's behavior is suspicious, but we don't know the motivation. Why did he have to kill his wife?

"Then all of a sudden, we hear about Nitsos's affair with Katina. She appeared before you, gentlemen of the jury, and confirmed that, on the very same night of the murder, she met with Nitsos. He told her—and he himself admits this—to keep quiet, even if, 'they remove your teeth,' and even if, 'they cut your throat...'

"Why did he tell her this? Katina had an invitation to go to America, but Nitsos wouldn't let her go, taking advantage of his authority. Clearly he was infatuated with her. And as we understand his motive, Nitsos looks guiltier than ever to us. Of course that is not enough for the police. They do their duty. They pursue others. They interrogate Vasilios, and are convinced that Vasilios is innocent. Similarly, they establish the innocence of Pagonis and Zanias. Then they turn their attention toward the question of the murder weapon. All the shotguns in the village are examined, and the only gun that has been fired recently is Socrates Karaiskos's. The shell found at the crime scene came from his gun. So Karaiskos is placed under arrest as a suspect. From that moment, gentlemen of the jury, justice has pursued the people who committed the crime.

"When the injured Panayota said, 'Vasilios has killed us,' Konandreas intervened to say, 'Vasilios didn't kill you; I told you who would.' Nitsos says he was informed of what Konandreas said. But Nitsos didn't communicate with any third person to find that out. And even if he did, why didn't he say this to the police at the time? Because the moment Nitsos heard that phrase by Konandreas, he was overtaken by shivers and fainting fits. He extended his hands for the police to put the handcuffs on. At that moment, Nitsos saw himself in front of the firing squad. At that moment, gentlemen of the jury, Nitsos admitted his guilt with his behavior.

"The time has come for us to stop the criminal activities of a person who has had brushes with the law since his youth. Nitsos is the Rustler of Patras, the Murderer of Panayota, the man who strikes Poly and makes Katina a moral wreck. The same Nitsos has tried to appear here as a man of honor, attacking Konandreas all the time. If it was not for Konandreas, we would not have had the criminals apprehended by the law.

"Gentlemen of the jury! You have also heard the prosecution tear to pieces the ludicrous fabrications that the defense has made about Konandreas: that he is a Communist; that he conspired with the Communist Party of Greece to kill Nitsos; that on the night of the crime, he missed Nitsos and killed his own cousin, Panayota. These are more examples of Nitsos's desperate attempts to evade justice.

"Gentlemen of the jury! With his testimony, Nitsos confirmed his culpability. In addition to his remarks about Konandreas, he lashed out against government employees, policemen, and anyone else who tried to find the truth.

"Gentlemen of the jury, the public prosecutor's bench asks of you with unshaken conviction to sentence the accused. This conviction is supported by the court records and the documents that have been presented here. We don't wish for Nitsos's destruction. We have no reason to be vengeful, though his fellow villagers seem to be so, and with good reason, for no one has spread as much evil in that small community as George Nitsos. For us, Nitsos is a Greek citizen who should be protected by Greek laws until proven guilty. And guilty he has been proven now.

"Gentlemen of the jury! May God and His sacred Gospel lead us. Gentlemen, you swore with your right hand raised that you would follow this case with the greatest attention and reach your verdict with honor and conscience. From that moment, gentlemen of the jury, honorable citizens of Halkida, you were separated from your fellow citizens and became the official members of this court. You were adorned with the authority of Greek justice.

"Honorable citizens of Halkida, if you asked me what I would consider the greatest honor in life to be, I would answer that there is no bigger honor than being one of you. This is because the decision you have to make is momentous, especially in the wake of an earlier jury's verdict on this case that stirred the righteous indignation of the entire Greek nation. When that first gunshot was fired on the defenseless, honorable, and virtuous Panayota Nitsos, its echoes were heard not just among those remote mountains but in the entire Hellenic World and beyond."

Papandreou finished his closing argument by advising the jury to ignore anything that the defense called "extenuating circumstances." This, Thanasis knew, meant he was suggesting that no punishment— not even the death penalty—would be too harsh for George and Socrates.

CHAPTER 50:
A MARRIAGE MADE IN HEAVEN

AFTER PAPANDREOU DELIVERED HIS CLOSING argument, the attorneys on the prosecution team followed with remarks of their own, each man contributing to a narrative that slowly and methodically dismantled the defense.

They painted George Nitsos as a repeat offender who had broken the law on numerous occasions, as a womanizer who had treated his wife with unusual cruelty and contempt, and as a coward who had for years conspired to have his wife murdered. George's litany of explanations and counter-accusations, they argued, was confused, contradictory, and haphazard. He was a man willing to do or say anything to stay out of jail, a man who for years had relied on his charm and political clout to get his way.

George's motives, the prosecution argued, were not difficult to understand. He was angry with Panayota because she couldn't bear him children, and he was in love with Katina, who he had prevented from going to America, had warned to remain silent about their affair, and had promised he would marry as soon as he was out of jail.

As for the murder itself, it had clearly been premeditated, with George arranging things to make sure that he—and he alone—was alone with Panayota as they walked a narrow and treacherous footpath in the dark. Ballistic experts had proven that, contrary to George's claims, the two had walked in single file, not side-by-side, with Panayota out front and illuminated by George's flashlight.

The shell from Socrates's shotgun, meanwhile, had only been called into question after George's attorneys had grown desperate. Had it been substituted, as the defense claimed, why had there been no mention of the discrepancy until just before the Athens trial? And how had such a feat been accomplished under the nose of the police captain, a loyal friend of George Nitsos?

The prosecution also laid bare Socrates's flimsy alibi. He could not be accounted for between the hours of 8:30 p.m. and 1:00 a.m. His decision to call out to a fellow shepherd in the wee hours of the morning looked, in retrospect, like a transparent attempt to establish his presence on the hills outside of the village. Likewise, the dead partridge, un-plucked and uneaten, only cast more suspicion on him. If his gun was all but unusable, how had he managed to kill the bird? And why had he left the bird in its state, unless he had planned to use it to prop up his alibi?

The prosecution, after arguing that the murder belonged to a longstanding pattern of abuse and neglect, finished by reading a letter from George's father, which he had written in response to a letter from Paraskevi after the murder:

I'm curious to know why you make all these complaints to me when you know that I have no responsibility whatsoever in this business. I left George as an eight – year-old, and when he grew up, you made him your son-in-law by force. You lived around him for the past fourteen years, and now you tell me about my "prodigal son." Were you not there to see what was going on?

If, as you say, my son is such a good-for-nothing, why didn't you tell your daughter: "My child, this is no life for you. Leave that awful man. We can do without all this luxury. Let us go back to our home and eat our vegetables together"?

But you did not. And now, after fourteen years, you tell me that my son is no good. I sent them a letter some years back, asking them to get a divorce since they could not live peacefully together. And do you know what they both answered? They wrote, "We're doing very well together. People say those things because they are jealous."

Now that you have killed Panayota and got my son into jail, you write to tell me that you didn't see what was coming and that my son is a murderer. You are the murderer. You have killed your own daughter.

You have locked us out of our own house, as well, just when we were planning to visit our relatives there. I don't know what you hope to achieve with all this, but I hope it makes you feel lighter in your heart.

Now your destiny is to cry like the partridge, because you, too, were only able to see so far and no further.
With sympathy from all of us,
Ioannes Nitsos

George Nitsos, the prosecution put it to the jury, wanted everyone to believe his marriage had been made in heaven. But did anyone think he was telling the truth?

CHAPTER 51:
THE BEST DEFENSE

"George Nitsos is a hero," Pan Gunaris proclaimed, pausing to read the reactions of the onlookers to the opening line of his closing argument for the defense. "George Nitsos is a hero," he repeated. "He was in the forefront of the war against the Communists. As the commander of the band in his district, he fought for the liberties we have today. If a man like him, a man of the mountains, unchecked and free, had never shown any propensity for cruelty and had never committed arbitrary acts of violence, why would he suddenly develop such a propensity?

"Nitsos was held in very high esteem in Kupaki. He was the elected village council president, a post that is constantly under public scrutiny. In order to tarnish this image and make him look like a common criminal, the prosecutor looked desperately for something in Nitsos's past and gleefully discovered an old conviction from his youth—a conviction for rustling that is totally unrelated to this case.

"The accusation that Nitsos showed a strange inertia after the crime and did not chase the killer is ill-considered. Had he staged the whole incident, as the prosecution argues, he would have put on a show of heroism and pursued the gunman. It's precisely because he didn't organize the shooting that he behaved like a normal man in a crisis, a man whose wife was fatally wounded, a man who trauma had rendered inactive. He was not guilty of the murder, and therefore he didn't think it necessary to deflect suspicion from himself. And that's exactly why it didn't strike him that he ought to exploit the advantage his wife gave him by saying, 'Vasilios has killed us.'

"As for Socrates Karaiskos, the entire prosecution team couldn't succeed in burying the fact that he has never in his life done anything remotely criminal. An orphan, he overcame his vulnerable social position by hard work and determination. It was only after helping his two sisters get married and establish themselves that he started a family of his own. Why would such a caring family man suddenly get it into his head to throw all this away and turn into a killer for a few drachmas?"

Thanasis grimaced. It was obvious the defense wasn't about to yield an inch to the prosecution. On the contrary, Gunaris was airing a full-throated defense.

"The prosecution claims that the shell found at the crime scene came from Karaiskos's shotgun," the defense attorney continued. How could men with the military experience of Nitsos and Karaiskos not have found ways to destroy or dispose of such revealing evidence? The police captain discovered this much celebrated shell a full twelve hours after the crime, after the entire village of Kupaki had trampled over the crime scene. Anyone wishing to incriminate Karaiskos and Nitsos could easily have planted the shell there. The shell was not sent for fingerprinting. Instead, the captain carried it from house to house, leaving it on the investigation desks, to which Konandreas, who had become his shadow by now, had unchecked access.

"The shell sent to the forensic laboratory as evidence was not the shell found at the crime scene. This is a very crucial point. I cannot stress it enough. If it cannot be proven beyond doubt that a certain shell was actually found at the murder scene, then it follows that the gun it was fired from cannot be proven beyond doubt to be the murder weapon, therefore the owner of the gun cannot be accused of murder.

"The way the police captain conducted his investigation in Kupaki leaves much to be desired. He slept in Vasilios's house on the day he arrived there. Did he not think for a moment that he would be compromising the investigation by accepting the hospitality of a suspect? Surely he had heard by then that Panayota had named Vasilios before she died.

"Our well-known forensic expert has told you in the presence of other forensic experts that from six yards away—the distance the round was supposed to have been fired from—and on a terrain with a gradient of thirty-five degrees, which exactly describes the murder scene, Karaiskos's shotgun would have made a wound of more than twenty-two centimeters in diameter. The abdominal wounds which Panayota Nitsos succumbed to were only fourteen centimeters in diameter.

"Nitsos was injured by three bullets hitting different parts of his body. If one of them had hit him in the carotid artery or penetrated his abdomen and the peritoneum, he would have died with Panayota. Some of Nitsos's wounds were not very far away from these parts. Why would Nitsos take such a risk, trusting the marksmanship of the gunman he had allegedly hired, to prove that he is innocent? If Nitsos had died, would anyone have dared accuse him? And we know now how close he was to dying."

Thanasis rolled his eyes. George's wounds had hardly amounted to a scratch. The small rips in his pants had appeared self-inflicted—most likely the result of walking into a thorny bush before going to the Zakkases—and had required no medical attention from the doctor.

"Panayota lived for more than half an hour after being shot," Gunaris continued. "If Nitsos had organized the shooting, would he have let her live that long? Would he not have worried whether she had recognized Karaiskos in the light of the flash from the gun when it was fired at her? Would he not have stopped her from revealing any information to the villagers who had come to help her if he thought that this information could be potentially damaging to him? If Nitsos was the organizer of the crime, why would he be content with an injured Panayota when he could have had a dead Panayota by the time the villagers arrived? All he had to do was to tell Karaiskos, if Karaiskos had indeed done the shooting at his behest, to finish Panayota off.

If Karaiskos was the killer, would he have climbed down to the village the next day, carrying his gun over his shoulder, ready to present it to the waiting police?

"To get our answers, let us turn our attention away from Nitsos and Karaiskos and focus it on Konandreas, a man who stands to gain huge benefits if Nitsos is convicted."

Predictable, Thanasis thought. *Their best defense is to shift the blame onto someone else.*

"Sole proprietorship of the store in the village center," Gunaris said, still hammering away, "sole ownership of livestock hitherto jointly owned, the presidency of the village council—the list is long. After Nitsos was taken out of the picture, Konandreas became the uncrowned king of Kupaki and the area around it. But Greek justice will not let him deceive her. He will not only have to account for the crime of murdering Panayota, but also for that of looting George Nitsos's wealth. After the trial of Nitsos versus the people of Greece, you may well see the trial of Konandreas versus Nitsos and Konandreas versus the people of Greece.

"Let us now move on to Vasilios. The phrase, 'Vasilios has killed us,' that was uttered by the victim has not been properly understood by the unqualified people who took over this case. The interrogators asked the wrong questions. The investigators did not know what to look for. With the clarity of vision—and this has been scientifically proven—that comes to people in a crisis, Panayota had put two and two together, seen the whole plot, and realized who her murderer was, but it was too late to be of any help to her.

"The most tangible proof of Nitsos' innocence is not his own conduct after the murder but the conduct of Konandreas. He presents himself as already possessing the knowledge that Nitsos would be the killer, yet he had been silent for years until the murder. And his witnesses testify that he told the dying victim, 'Vasilios didn't kill you; I told you who would.' What a heartless thing to say to a dying woman! The question we all have to ask is not why Nitsos showed inertia during a life-threatening crisis, but why Konandreas showed inertia for so many years when he knew, in his own words, who would kill Panayota.

"If it were not for Katina, suspicion would have been focused relentlessly on Konandreas. The murder scene is located between his house and the house of his mother-in-law, Aggeliki Gumas. He passed the spot only fifteen minutes before the first shot at eleven p.m. In fact, he walked barely five feet away from where the killer would place himself to shoot at Panayota. Could he have cold-bloodedly set up the scene for the murder before going home to his wife and children? At the precise moment of the crime, his wife was on the balcony of his house and his mother-in-law at the window of her house. Were they waiting for something?

"The letter from Nitsos's father to Panayota's mother that was triumphantly read aloud here by the prosecution does not reveal the fissures in the relationship between George Nitsos and Panayota Nitsos, as the prosecution would have us believe. It reveals the burning envy of a section of the villagers of Kupaki—the envy that continues to manifest itself in the baseless allegations against Socrates Karaiskos and George Nitsos that you have listened to here.

"The mistake made in Athens was not the jury's decision to acquit the accused, but the court's decision to call the jury's verdict *peplanimeni*—in other words, a judicial error!

"Gentlemen of the jury! Nitsos and Karaiskos are not here before you as guilty men but as innocent citizens of Greece whose rights you have a duty to protect. A verdict for their acquittal has been issued from a court similar to this one. The disgruntled prosecution called those Athenian jurors incapable. They now praise you and flatter you with the same cynicism. They feel they can make you pass the verdict they want you to pass by fooling you into believing that you will be seen as the 'clean jury' from the real Greece, the great town of Halkida, as opposed to the 'corrupt jury' in the corrupt capital. They think that you're vain enough to say, 'We're better, and we're going to prove our superiority with a decision that will be diametrically opposed to that of the Athenian jury, a decision that will be popular with many people and segments of the press.'

"Gentlemen of the jury! The opinion of the judges, who have also complimented you here in court, is insignificant. That's why the legislators determined that you, the people, are going to decide, and not the judges. Because you decide as free citizens of Greece, whereas they decide as officials of the legal system.

"Countless innocent lives, victims of judicial errors, have been destroyed ever since the start of our legal system because of officials seeing no further than the letter of the law. You have the choice to look beyond books and see the human side of justice. You have the choice to be the kind face of Greek justice that emphasizes the protection of the innocent. You have the choice not to be the harsh mask of the law that has to make an example by punishing—and often punishing the weak and the innocent in its zeal.

"The defense team joins me in imploring you not to wash your hands of your moral duty like Pontius Pilate. Our constitution and our laws protect the personal freedoms of the Greek citizens by having juries deciding the outcome of important trials.

"Gentlemen of the jury." Gunaris dropped his voice to an audible whisper. "You're answerable only before God, for He is the voice of your honor and your conscience."

Gunaris spoke for several hours that day, but before the trial was over, each member of the defense team would have a chance to address the jury at length. All went fairly smoothly for the defense—until Palos stood to make his closing remarks.

CHAPTER 52:
THEATRICS

PALOS, WHO THANASIS HAD ALWAYS considered the foremost attorney on the defense's team, if not in all of Greece, was losing it. Instead of wrapping up his closing argument, he was getting bogged down in petty matters that made him look desperate.

"The prosecutor has met the police major outside the court and conversed with him," Palos said angrily. "I have myself seen this."

"There's no law that says the public prosecutor can't talk to a police major, Counsel," Judge Demopoulos replied mildly.

"I'm surprised by the indulgence with which this court seems to view the prosecution's dubious conduct," Palos shot back. "The prosecutor himself spares no efforts to compliment the bench, speaking scornfully about the court in Athens in order to make this one feel important. Speaking of jurors, chosen by the criminal justice system of Greece, as bank employees without legal knowledge is too much to countenance."

"Pray refresh my memory about this particular instance," the judge said.

"Your Honor, I refer to the incident, which should be in the court records, when the prosecutor said that seven out of ten of the jurors of that court were bank employees."

"I see nothing wrong with that. It was a statement of fact."

"But it was a statement of fact made in a derogatory tone."

"We deal with *facts* here in this court, Counsel. We shall leave *tones* to acting schools and the like."

"Yet any acting school would be proud of our prosecutor. He's a glorious orator, but with little evidence or logic to complement his oratory excesses, which are a study in verbal acrobatics—exactly what one would expect from someone who's in love with himself and suffers from autism."

Papandreou stood. "Permission to speak, Your Honor."

"Granted."

"I'd like to have these malignant words, which incidentally best describe Mr. Palos's client, who he seems desperate to save from a just conviction, added to the court records."

The attorneys then traded jabs, and Thanasis looked on in disbelief as Palos alleged that someone unknown to him was following him daily and that he had complained to the public prosecutor about it. Next, he began reading from a book about fingerprints, stating that the captain of the county police investigating the case should have read a copy before investigating. He then pivoted to Goethe, the famous German poet, who he said had not cried when his child had died, just as George Nitsos had not shed a tear for Panayota in her final hour. And soon he was reciting Greek romantic poetry as he described the "true love" between George and Panayota.

It was all Thanasis could do not to laugh. The defense attorney appeared to have combed the world's greatest literature in order to save George from the firing squad.

Palos, however, was just getting started. By the time he had finished his oratory, he had eulogized his own dead parents, who had left behind three orphaned girls.

Thanasis leaned closer at the sight of Palos wiping away a tear.

While the attorney's performance impressed at least one teary-eyed juror, it fell flat with Judge when Palos announced he would do whatever he could to avoid ever appearing in another case presided over by him.

The judge, who had by now already begun disciplinary action against Palos, responded by calling his comments inappropriate. "I'm going to report you to the Bar of Halkida," he said icily.

He then addressed the rest of the court. "With the patently false accusations that the defense attorney has leveled against most of us here, his own profile appears more and more like that of his client, who is aptly called Linatsas."

He's right, Thanasis thought. Was Palos delusional? Or was all of this a strategy by the clever attorney to influence the jurors by whatever means possible, given that a juror, who Thanasis knew was a retired military officer apparently toughened by his career, cried along with him?

"Lukas," Polyxeni said to me one afternoon when she could no longer take the constant nagging from Mitros and Papazois, "go fetch us a newspaper. Otherwise these two will give me no peace."

"If you see Father Kritsas," Papazois said, "remember to thank him again for the newspaper the other day."

I nodded and hurried off to Krokylion, where another large crowd had gathered in the café to wait for the newspaper bus. While I was waiting for the bus, others who were waiting made some comments supporting Nitsos and Karaiskos and against my father. They were very upsetting.

As soon as the papers arrived, I bought one and raced to Kupaki. The tears I had kept in check poured freely down my cheeks.

Not long after turning onto the cobblestone path toward the village, I caught sight of a tall man plowing a field with two mules. He was holding a whip in one hand and gripping the handle of a plow with the other. An older woman, most likely his wife, was following him and spreading seeds in the furrows. It was Father Kritsas, with his vestment pulled up and tied to his back. His priest's hat was nowhere in sight.

"*Papuli*," I hollered as the mules turned to make another run in the opposite direction.

"Yes?" He pulled hard, lifting the entire plow in the air and turning it so he could face me. "Oh, it's you again!" he said, panting from the exertion.

"*Papuli*," I said, "Papazois told me to thank you for the *Ethnos* you gave me to give to him the other day."

With rivulets of sweat running down his face and into his beard and the hair on his chest, Father Kritsas reached over the fence and enveloped the back of my head with his huge hands, holding them there.

I made no effort to escape. I felt comforted by the old man's touch.

"Your father is good," he said. "He has them this time."

The fears I had felt just minutes earlier at the café evaporated in the gentle spring breeze.

CHAPTER 53:
MESSAGE FROM DARKNESS_
DARKNESS OVERCOME?

THE LAST OF THE CLOSING arguments were finished by eleven o'clock in the evening on April 6, 1955 at which point Thanasis left the court with his sister Aggelo and Aunt Paraskevi.

When they reached the seafront, they found the streets silent, save for the waves of the straits breaking gently on the shore. The early spring air was mild, and the only illumination besides the moonlight came from the lamp posts along the promenade. Thanasis, as he watched the light play on the crests of the waves, thought he could go on forever watching the light reflections. The sea had always fascinated him. Was it because he hailed from the mountains? All he knew for sure was he could unwind now, safe in the knowledge that he had done all he could do for Panayota. He let the moonlight drive his worries away. The case was beyond his control now and would be decided by the jury.

A majestic castle stood guard over the town, towering atop the hill across the straits, and Thanasis couldn't help fancying that it, too, was affected by all this serenity, but soon he could feel the familiar anxieties edging their way into his mind. He walked toward their hotel with a sigh. It had been good while it lasted.

The three slept in the same room together and were soon sound asleep, their fatigue having stolen every last ounce of energy.

The next morning, Thanasis awoke to sunlight on his face as the sun crested the hill in the east. He needed coffee. He rose to get himself a strong cupful, making special pains not to wake the others.

Aggelo stirred in the bed. She was smiling at him. "Let me tell you about the dream I had," she said before he could ask her if she wanted coffee. "Let me tell you who came to me in my dream."

Aunt Paraskevi grunted, having been so rudely jarred from her sleep.

"Your late husband, of course," Thanasis replied. Who else but her husband could have appeared in her dreams? He'd been doing so for the last several years.

"No" Aggelo said. "It was Panayota."

"Oh?" Thanasis didn't know what else to say.

"And they will be convicted."

"I'm sure it will come true," Thanasis said, unable to resist mocking his sister.

"This was different," Aggelo insisted. "It was so real. She was very clear about the conviction."

"Oh… oh… my child!" Aunt Paraskevi obviously didn't share Thanasis's cynicism. "Was she all right, Aggelo?"

"It was at our field in outside the village," Aggelo said and began to narrate her dream to her captive audience of two. "She was opposite, standing in the neighbors' field. She called across to me. 'Aggelo! Aggelo!' And I responded. I asked her where she'd been."

By now, Paraskevi was crying. "Where had she been? Oh, where?"

"She wouldn't tell me, Aunt. Are you going to let me finish?"

Paraskevi blew her nose and waited in silence for Aggelo to finish the story.

The crux of the narration was that Panayota and the "others"—whoever they were—were "preparing" for Linatsas. They had made all necessary "arrangements" to "take care" of him.

Thanasis wasn't sure how the phrase was meant to be interpreted. "Was Panayota saying she'd take care of George in the hereafter the way she did during their marriage?" he asked his sister. "Or was she implying they would make him pay for all the suffering he caused her?"

"I don't know, Brother," Aggelo answered. "I'm just repeating exactly what she said."

Thanasis had never considered himself superstitious and therefore treated Aggelo's dream like a joke. However, he had to admit that he found comfort in a message from the other world predicting George's conviction. That said, he was unwilling to leave anything to chance.

"Find a seat in the front row," he advised his aunt later that morning. "Directly opposite the jury bench. And do stare at the jurors constantly. Make eye contact. Make it difficult for them to avoid your eyes. Make sure they see Panayota in them."

The foreman of the jury stepped forward. He and his fellow jury members had been deliberating since half past ten in the evening. Now, two and a half hours later, the crowd that had filled the courtroom beyond capacity and spilled out into the grounds was stirring impatiently. Thanasis, surveying the whole scene from his front-row seat, realized that everyone on hand, even the latecomers behind him jostling for a better view, was waiting for closure.

"With honor and conscience," the foreman began, "a verdict has been reached by the majority of the jury."

The courtroom fell silent as those in the crowd leaned forward and strained to hear the foreman's words.

"Both of the accused, George Nitsos and Socrates Karaiskos, have been found guilty. While their mental state at the time can't be called insanity, their capacity to fully understand the injustice of their actions was considerably diminished..."

The foreman's words were lost in the cheerings of the crowd, though some grumbles and protests could also be heard. Despite the noise from the crowd, Thanasis could make out the gist of the jury's decision. George was sentenced to twenty years in jail. Socrates earned eighteen years and one month, the latter being for his illegal use of a firearm. Both were to lose their political rights for a period of ten years, during which time they would not be allowed to vote from prison. They were also to pay the court expenses jointly. Finally, the court ruled that they were to pay Papaskevi, ten thousand drachmas for the mental agony their actions had brought upon her.

"You have five days to appeal against this decision," Judge Demopoulos said, addressing the two defendants.

Palos shot to his feet. "The defense fully intends to appeal against this unjust decision."

A vindicated Aggelo, who along with Paraskevi was seated beside Thanasis, turned to him. "See, Brother," she said. "You mocked me when I said that Panayota came to me in my dreams and told me about the verdict."

Paraskevi, silent until now, spoke. "That man from the jury said that they were guilty. If they know those bastards killed my daughter, why aren't they being shot dead?"

Papandreou and Kokkinos stood just a few feet away, surrounded by members of the jury, who were talkative now and appeared just as relieved as everyone else that a decision had been made.

Marmaras, the defense attorney from Halkida, called to Thanasis across the court. "Are you happy with the verdict this time, Mr. Konandreas?"

"Mr. Marmaras," Thanasis hollered back, "pleased I am, but satisfied I'm not. They'll go to jail for a few years and will be among us again one day. Panayota can never be with us again. They should pay for their crime and suffer the same way my cousin did."

One of the jurors, approached Thanasis. "That's what I would have liked, too," he said.

In fact, as Thanasis learned a short while later from his local attorney, a few jurors had proposed even the death sentence, but the majority had vetoed it.

It was late, nearly three o'clock in the morning, when Thanasis, Aggelo, and Aunt Paraskevi were walking on the seafront towards their hotel.

Aggelo pointed her finger at the full moon, cutting through the overcast skies and brightening the cityscape. "Where were you the night poor Panayota was shot, and I was running to the Gumas house nearly killing myself in the darkness?"

Photo on left: Moon on the night of the murder, September 6-7, 1953.

Photo on right: Moon on decision night, April 7-8. 1955.

CHAPTER 54:
THE TELEGRAM

THE CHURCH BELLS RANG THAT morning at eight o'clock, signaling the students to assemble in front of the school. After a brief prayer, we queued up for breakfast, which had been prepared by one of the mothers.

The sun was already warming the air, and I felt cheerful as I stood in line to have my cup filled. Ahead of me, steam rose from a huge vat, whose contents, a mixture of water, powdered milk, and sugar, simmered over a steady burning fire.

Just as I neared the front of the line, my great-uncle's voice boomed from the direction of our house. That was nothing new. Mitros often cursed his wife or shouted at the goat.

I had barely begun to drink my milk when Polyxeni appeared on the path, walking briskly toward the school. I hurried to meet her, as did my brothers and our teacher.

"What news, Polyxeni?" the teacher asked. "Anything from Halkida yet?"

"Yes!" Mother called out cheerfully. "Thanasis sent me this telegram," she said and waved the piece of paper in the air like a flag. "Guilty! They've been convicted. They'll be sent to prison."

I felt an overwhelming urge to scream and shout but resisted.

"Good, good!" the teacher said in a jubilant voice. Then his smile faded. "Is that why Mitros was screaming a while ago from his house? Did he beat me on the bet?"

"I'm afraid he did, teacher. The big guy got twenty years, and the sidekick eighteen."

"Oh no!" the teacher lamented, sounding more pleased than someone who had just lost a bet should. "Please tell Mitros I'll pass that way to see him, will you?"

As we continued with our meal, some of the students began making quick calculations.

"I'll be thirty years old when they come out," one said.

"I'll have a wife and two sons," said another.

"Too bad they didn't get the firing squad."

Although overjoyed by the news, I felt another emotion, one I hadn't anticipated: sympathy. I hadn't shown it during the trial, but now I worried on behalf of the students whose families had supported George and Socrates.

That afternoon, when I arrived home from school, everybody appeared content, but there were no loud cheers of celebration.

The teacher arrived next door a few minutes later to visit Mitros and admit defeat. "Congratulations, old man," he said and produced a hundred drachma bill from his pocket. "Here's the money I owe you."

Mitros, despite looking ill, appeared happy about the outcome of the trial. "Don't worry about the money," he said, waving away the bill. He gestured toward his hives. "You've given me more help and encouragement with those babies than a hundred drachmas can buy."

It was the Friday before Palm Sunday, and Mother had us children in church that evening. After services, although everyone knew about the court's decision, no one openly spoke about it. Most seemed quietly content with the verdict, and only a handful approached Polyxeni to quietly whisper their satisfaction. The less said about the matter, most seemed to think, the better for everyone.

PART VI:
LIFE AFTER THE COURTS

CHAPTER 55:
THE BONES OF THE DEAD

HOLY WEEK ARRIVED. FATHER WAS home, and along with fasting and joining the family for church services nearly every day, he was assessing his financial troubles. He was very thankful that his attorneys had reduced their fee to a mere fraction of what was customary at the time. It was an act of generosity, Thanasis thought, disproving the commonly held notion that lawyers were heartless. That had certainly helped, but he knew he was penniless.

I was at the store one day that week helping my father when two prosecution witnesses who had spent their own money at Halkida came to the store. Thanasis asked me to pay them with money from the store's counter. To his great embarrassment, there was not enough cash in the counter or his pocket to pay both of them back. He was forced to ask one to wait a few days.

"I can't believe this has happened to us," my father said softly after the men had left. "I have never been left without money my entire life. I've always had some, even when I was a young shepherd. And now this has happened to me."

Thanasis was certainly a tightfisted trader with sound business instincts and a head for arithmetic. He could impress customers, many of them far better educated than him, by working out percentages in his mind and offering them deals while they were still calculating. Perhaps because of his aptitude for math, he knew better than anyone the long odds he was facing regarding his children's education.

His children would have to move to a larger town for high school and pay for room and board. As for a university education, that was something only the rich in Greece could entertain. How would Thanasis possibly save enough money in such a short time to put his four children through school?

"When we had the means," his wife lamented one night, "we threw them into the straits of Halkida. I knew this was coming, but I couldn't stop it."

"I couldn't stop it, either," Thanasis responded. "But my children will go to university. God will help us find a way."

Determined not to let go his dream, even if he knew little of what it would take financially or if his children were even capable of pursuing a university education, he devised a long and arduous work schedule for the entire family. The children, besides being responsible for their schoolwork, worked sixteen-hour days that included laboring in the fields, doing household chores, helping with the bee-keeping, collecting milk from the family's shepherds, making cheese, and manning the village store.

Eleni, George's sister, returned to Kupaki just before summer, and my friends and I watched as the shutters of the Nitsos house were opened for the first time in nearly two years. It was rumored that George's parents would be staying there.

Along with the opening of Nitsos's house came a demand by Paraskevi, the mother of Panayota, that her daughter's dowry be returned. In a village where dowries only travelled in one direction— from the house of the bride to the house of the groom—this silent, desolate return of a dowry to the murdered woman's home was no small event.

We watched in stunned silence, several of the villagers crossing themselves in disbelief, as Panayota's dowry was marched back to the home of her mother. This was not the dowry of a rosy-cheeked village maid, but that of a murdered middle-aged woman. There was no suntanned, rough-handed, broad-shouldered groom dancing to clarinet music, leaping from boulder to boulder on the village path with the freedom of reckless youth. The dowry wasn't going to the groom's house, with his parents and siblings welcoming it, but to the old house of a buried bride, its only inhabitant a grieving old woman. Instead of the happy music of the clarinet, the wails of Paraskevi filled our ears.

A few days later, as the summer vacation drew near, my older brother Kostas and I climbed a pair of cherry trees after lunch at St. Anthony Cemetery and started filling ourselves with the delicious ripe fruit. We had only been there a few minutes when we caught sight of the diminutive figure of Papaskevi, Panayota's mother, who was holding a small sickle and a towel at the cemetery gate. She had come to clear her daughter's grave of the dry wild grass covering it and light a candle. Soon she was crying and talking to her daughter as she stood over the grave.

Kostas and I, no longer able to enjoy our feast, slid down from the trees, accidentally startling Paraskevi, who crossed herself fearfully.

"Aunt Paraskevi," I said after we climbed the lawn terraces and reached the path that led to the gate, "why have you got 'Panayota Soulias' instead of 'Panayota Nitsos' on the cross?"

"That was my daughter's name, my golden boy," she replied, her voice catching as she sobbed.

"Wasn't she Panayota Nitsos?" I persisted.

"No, no, my little one. She never was. She was always a Soulias."

Kostas spoke up. "But the papers were calling her Nitsos, not Soulias, weren't they?"

"I don't know about the papers, but I'll never let her have that bastard's name in the other world. Never!" Paraskevi studied us a moment. "Have your parents never told you how bad it is to eat cherries from cemetery trees?"

"No," I said, my mind struggling to make a connection between this and Panayota's last name. "Why?"

Paraskevi responded by lecturing us on how bad it was to eat cherries from trees growing inside the cemetery, which, as she put it, "belonged to the dead."

I tried to counter with what I knew of gardening, citing various facts learned in school, but she turned a deaf ear to my comments.

"Did you eat the cherry pits, too?" Paraskevi asked.

The question unnerved me. "A few," I answered nervously. "At the beginning, when we first got here and ate quickly, we swallowed a few."

Kostas nodded gravely.

"Oh ... no ... my children!" Paraskevi shook her head and clicked her tongue. "Those are the bones of the dead, and you have swallowed them?"

A wave of nausea washed over me. Without another word, I hurried home, leaving a puzzled Kostas behind. I bit down the fear and disgust that threatened to overpower me as I ran, managing to keep the cherries down all the way back. Once I reached home, they all came out, and I felt like my insides were being shoveled out, much like the dirt mixed with bones that had been flung from Socrates's spade when he had dug Panayota's grave the day after the murder.

It took a lot of reassurance from my parents and grandmother to put my mind at rest.

CHAPTER 56:
THE NIGHT VISIT

THE VILLAGE BEGAN TO HEAL that summer of 1955. The prosecution witnesses used the words *perjurer* and *corrupt* less and less when referring to the defense witnesses, who, since George and Socrates's conviction, had been bending over backward to treat the prosecution witnesses respectfully. Thanasis seemed to be letting go, too. Only Miltiades Zakkas, George's brother-in-law, still earned his ire. He couldn't forgive him for the things he'd said in court. Zakkas had called Thanasis, among other things, a Communist, which was a serious accusation and one that could affect not only him but us kids, as well, since such labels often followed a person over the course of his or her career.

We were finishing dinner around the fireplace one evening that autumn when someone knocked on the front door.

"Who is it?" Father asked as he approached the small hallway to open the door.

"Alex Nitsos and Eleni," a man said from outside. It was George's brother and sister.

Father and Mother exchanged glances.

"Are we still allowed into your house?" Eleni asked.

Thanasis opened the door wide. "Of course," he said. "Come right in."

Alex, who had returned from America earlier that year, had driven into the village in his brand-new purple Lincoln with a white top, the wide-eyed villagers looking on in amazement. I had never expected him to come to our house. My parents, too, looked utterly surprised.

Alex and Eleni entered, and my parents offered them seats near the fireplace.

"Time for bed," Father said.

My siblings and I, who had been sitting beside the fire and pretending not to be sleepy, reluctantly shuffled off for bed. This was one adult conversation we wouldn't be allowed to hear.

As Alex and Eleni took a couple of the places we children had vacated, Thanasis reflected on the similarities between George and his brother. Funny, talented with a guitar in his hands or a vocal melody on his lips—Alex was just as entertaining as his jailed brother, but he had something George did not: sincerity. He was also less vulgar. Even the most puritanical members of the community had no reason to think harshly of Alex Nitsos.

Alex was direct. "We decided to visit you at night," he said, "because we didn't want people to see us."

"We want to put this thing behind us and build bridges," Eleni said in an apologetic tone that took Thanasis off guard. "If we've done anything unforgivable toward you, we're truly sorry."

Polyxeni excused herself and returned a few minutes later with a tray stacked with homemade bread, feta cheese, walnuts, chestnuts, and grilled herring. She also brought homemade wine.

"Perhaps too late," Alex said, "but we know the truth now."

"Panayota was the best wife any man could have," Eleni added, her eyes moist with tears. "But George is our brother, and there was nothing else we could think of at the time but to believe in his innocence and support him. We had no choice. No other option even entered our minds at the time."

Did she believe her brother was a wife-killer? It seemed to Thanasis that she was coming awfully close to admitting such a thing.

As the night progressed, Alex drank glass after glass of the homemade wine, which loosened his tongue.

"Do you know, Thanasis," he began, his words slightly slurred, "I was the one who urged Panayota to be brave and do something to break up the relationship between Poly and George. And she took my advice." He paused for another sip of wine and then hiccupped. "She intercepted that letter he had sent to that girl and read it aloud in the village square. Hats off to her. It wasn't timidity that made her stay with George; it was love. And my brother didn't deserve it. No, he didn't deserve it.

"We were *this* close," Alex continued, trying to focus his eyes on the thumb and index finger of his left hand. "We were *this* close to using our contacts to persuade, perhaps even *buy* that juror in Athens who wouldn't go with the rest of the jury. That would have put an end to it all, and there would have been no grounds for the case to be sent to Halkida."

Thanasis knew now that the only juror in Athens to dissent in the case was an independent and honorable man, but was not sure if he had ever been approached by his side. "Well," he said, "good for you that you didn't get any closer. If that juror was who I think he was, he would have been too honorable to be for sale, and you would now be behind bars with your brother."

Alex nodded, while Eleni remained silent.

Thanasis had no doubt that it wasn't the drink talking; Alex was telling them the truth. In fact, later that year, a cousin of George's would actually name the figure that they'd been prepared to offer the juror: twenty thousand drachmas.

"Eleni and I are now planning to sell our houses in the city," Alex continued. "There's no other way we'll be able to afford the legal fees for both trials."

"Tell me about it," Thanasis said dryly.

"He's left me a poor man," Alex said. "My brother has left me a poor man, Thanasis."

Thanasis couldn't help thinking that the poverty of Alex Nitsos, living in Michigan and driving from Athens in his purple and white Lincoln convertible, was quite different from his own.

He noticed the skies brightening outside. It was almost dawn.

"If he left you a poor man, Alex" he said, laughing bitterly, "I'll need to find another word for what he has turned me into." He nodded to the tray Polyxeni had brought out hours earlier. "Have some of that herring. It was grilled right here at this fireplace."

CHAPTER 57:
AT LAST A DOWRY!

"You murderer!" a woman screamed. "You dare come back here? Get lost, you... you son of the devil! Why didn't you go to hell, never to return?"

By now many of the shuttered windows in Kupaki had been hurriedly thrown open. Heads poked forth to see what all the fuss was about. I joined a handful of men who rushed to the village square, where four paths met, and where Papadia, Papazois's wife, was giving Socrates Karaiskos an earful.

It was September, 1962. More than seven years had passed since the trial in Halkida. Socrates, having had his jail time reduced in exchange for his labor and good behavior, was back. Until now, he had managed to keep a low profile by avoiding the store and walking the paths only sparingly. This afternoon, he had apparently crossed paths with Papadia, who had refused to give him a wide berth. It was here, nearly two decades earlier, that Panayota had read aloud George's love letter to Poly, where George and Socrates had organized their wild revelry, complete with a donkey dressed in human clothes.

Socrates, rather than return Papadia's fire, uttered not a single word. Instead, he doubled his pace and strode quickly toward his home, where his wife, who also had heard the commotion, had come running out. She grabbed him when he reached the yard and pulled him inside.

For my part, I was now in my late teens. I'd just returned to the village from Athens, where we had lived since 1958. Having just taken the entrance test for the Medical School of the University of Athens, I was enjoying a brief vacation in Kupaki. A couple of weeks later, the news that I had passed the entrance test reached me, and I forgot all about Socrates's clash with Papadia. After my name was printed in the major Athenian dailies, which published all the names of the students who had gained admission to the various prestigious faculties of the university, congratulatory messages poured in from all directions from friends and relatives, close and distant.

But my celebratory mood vanished when I realized that I didn't have the money needed for books and tuition. My only hope was to find a job, but those, too, were hard to come by in the 1960s in Greece.

Fortunately, through the kindness of acquaintances, I found paid employment just before the academic year was to start. Despite having a job, I still had no tuition money for the first semester. How would I pay?

Just as I was running out of options, the right-wing government passed a law that made tuition for a university education free. The Communist Party of Greece had been asking for just such a law for several years, claiming that the Soviets enjoyed a free education. The Communists had been taking to the streets since early spring, chanting the slogan, "Free Paedia, no dowry for Sofia." Princess Sofia was the daughter of King Pavlos and Queen Frederica of Greece. Her marriage with King Carlos of Spain was being subsidized with substantial money from the Greek government. The money was called a present, but to the populace it was a dowry. Then there was the center coalition, led by George Papandreou, who was competing with the Communists for the Socialists' vote and who was promising the nation that, if elected, he would provide "free Paedia." With the freedom we enjoyed, he claimed, we would be "better off than the Soviets."

Now there was no need of tuition. Little did my late grandfather "Dowry Konandreas" know that, years after he had failed to get a good dowry for his son, his grandchild and the Queen of Spain would get from the same source a very good dowry indeed.

Later, I stumbled upon an enterprising way to pay for the additional expenses of medical school: I took notes at lectures, organized them, and typed them up, and they became quick reference texts sold to other students. I had my own money, a Volkswagen, and a small savings account, the latter of which I would one day use to pay for my transatlantic move. The future, precarious one moment, was suddenly smiling on me.

During sunset one sultry evening during the trip, I decided to light candles on the graves of departed loved ones at the St. Anthony's Cemetery outside the village.

The cherry trees, the fruit of which I'd once tasted before expelling it in a moment of fear and nausea, were long gone. Only dry grass and a stately row of cypresses remained to soften the imposing sea of marble tombs, the lonely chapel, and the enclosing stone wall. I could just make out the sound of children playing soccer in the village, their laughter interrupted every now and then by the candles crackling on the gravestones. A lizard scurried swiftly past. To the east loomed the top of St. Nicholas Hill. To the north, a smattering of red clay-tiled village rooftops could be seen in and amongst the trees.

As I stood over my father Thanasis's grave, I noticed a fascinating symmetry. Nine paces to his left was the grave of George Nitsos. Situated nine paces to the right was the grave of Panayota. Though the positioning was likely coincidental, it got me in a contemplative mood. What was Thanasis doing between them? Was he protecting Panayota from George? Was he keeping them apart as he had not done in 1935?

Had he done the latter, Panayota might have been free to marry a man worthy of her values. Her work ethic, her spirit, and her keen mind would have had a chance to flourish in the deep, nurturing soil of our village.

On the walk back towards my childhood home, I thought about how the community and culture had evolved since the days of the events with my father and Panayota in my story.

Kupaki has, for the most part, remained the same tiny village in the mountains. However, it has undergone substantial modernization from the time of Panayota's affair. Today a mother is as likely to fret over her daughter being hesitant to begin dating as she is to worry about her starting too soon.

How would Thanasis and Panayota fair in today's world? Would they have acted the same way in 2005 as they had in 1935? Would their adherence to tradition have been so steadfast?

I concluded that Thanasis and Panayota were modern incarnations of their resilient and cunning ancestors. Maybe, as in the tragedies of Ancient Greece, they were figures destined to fight for their honor, no matter how foolish the rest of the world may think them to be.

My sons, Johnathan and Peter, reminded me that when Helen was taken to Troy, her loved ones did not hesitate to sacrifice their wealth and safety. They launched a thousand ships and endured a decade of war, all to protect her honor.

EPILOGUE

"Mr. Marmaras, pleased I am, but satisfied I'm not. They'll go to jail for a few years and will be among us again one day. Panayota can never be with us again. They should pay for their crime and suffer the same way my cousin did."

That is what Thanasis answered back to defense attorney Marmaras immediately after the verdict was announced in Halkida, when he was asked in court, if he was pleased with the verdict.

Socrates Karaiskos would, in the years to come, emigrate with his wife and children to Canada, where he would carve out a modest life for himself and his family. His return trips to Kupaki over the years continued to earn him mostly enmity from the locals, who never forgot his conviction.

And what became of George Nitsos, the man behind Panayota's murder? The year was 1967. My parents had joined us kids in Athens since 1962. During lunch one Sunday, a distant relative telephoned and told Thanasis that George had been released from prison early because he had received credit for doing jail work as the jail's church custodian.

After his release, George opened a supermarket with the help of his remaining supporters, but that enterprise failed because, as one of his partners said later, he was cheating. He then traveled to Canada and then the U. S. for various adventures before eventually returning to Greece and ultimately Kupaki. I was shocked to learn that, after insinuating himself back into village life, he was eventually accepted by most in the village.

It wasn't long before he was a regular once again at the village store, where he told jokes and acted the part of the charismatic commander once again.

In the spring of 1985, Thanasis returned to Kupaki and wanted to pay his respects to a former mailman from nearby Krokylion who had served the village for many years and who had just passed away. Unable to find transportation from Kupaki to Krokylion, Thanasis, by now quite ill himself, embarked on the trip on foot, despite Polyxeni's pleas.

After a few days at the village, Father's health deteriorated further and he was forced to return to Athens for medical care. George, who was at the store when he heard the news, turned toward the church and crossed himself. "May St. George bring him back wrapped in white sheets," he said.

The remark, a reference to the tradition of bringing home in white sheets the body of someone who has died away from home, eventually found its way to Polyxeni's ears. Not normally one for confrontation and unable to find George, she asked a friend and neighbor of George to relay a message to him.

"Tell him," she said angrily, "that he was born Linatsas and will die Linatsas. Jail didn't help him change a bit. After all that has happened, he mentions Thanasis and wishes him death!"

Minutes later, George appeared at the front door of our house in the village and called Polyxeni out to talk. "Don't listen to the gossip and to what these bastards tell you here," he insisted. "It's all a lie. I didn't say anything about Thanasis."

"You talk to me like I don't know you!" Polyxeni shot back. "More than one person heard what you said."

"Thanasis shouldn't have gone on his own and on foot to Krokylion," George countered, "and I'm surprised you didn't prevent him from such a thoughtless task. That trip caused his illness."

By now Polyxeni was furious. "Thanasis put you in jail, and you dare speak his name? He is accomplished and is leaving good things behind. He has four children, eight grandchildren who care about him and protect him. What have you done? Who do you have? What are your creations? What legacy? What name? What are you going to leave behind when your day to go to St. Anthony's cemetery comes?"

In fact, George, to my knowledge, never mentioned Thanasis's name in public again. The day George was in his coffin however, on June 16, 1996, at the chapel of St. Anthony Cemetery, was an interesting one. Several people, including my Aunt Aggelo, who was living in California for many years and now visiting Kupaki, attended his funeral.

As soon as the priest started to give his blessing, the chapel walls began to shake. My aunt looked up and saw the rafters vibrating and the ceiling lamps swaying. Even the candles in the candelabras danced. A subterranean noise rumbled from beneath the chapel.

"Earthquake!" someone shouted before leading several in a mad dash for the exit.

Another jolt was felt a few minutes later at George's graveside.

AFTERWORD

IT HAS TAKEN ME YEARS to piece together this story to my satisfaction. I didn't want filial love to blind me to the truth, especially if the truth contradicted what I had been told by Thanasis and others close to me.

While in Greece in 2003, and while a photographer I had hired was busily taking photos of old newspapers for several days in the hallway of the National Library of Greece, I turned my attention to hunting down the court records. Did they still exist? I could only pray they did. But a phone call to the records department of the Greek Ministry of Justice didn't bode well.

"Court records? From the 1950s?"

I was met with incredulity. Didn't I know that records of court cases were destroyed after twenty-five years?

I refused to give up. Surely someone must have been lazy enough I thought, to leave a few dusty files undestroyed. My pursuit brought me to several old buildings in downtown Athens, and when I found myself in one on a narrow street near Omonoia Square, I began to wonder if I was crazy, after all.

A creaking elevator brought me to a small hallway. There I was met by a busy clerk who didn't bother to turn down his radio, which was playing a loud Greek bouzouki melody, when I explained what I had come to find. He shook his head, shrugged, and spread out his hands in helplessness, still humming, still listening to his radio.

I refused to leave, and finally he grew tired of the impasse and turned off the radio.

"Perhaps someone has forgotten to destroy them and they're somewhere," I said, making a last-ditch effort.

He disappeared for a while, and when he returned, he had two thick piles of typewritten records, which he tossed onto the counter, narrowly missing the radio.

"Police training material," he muttered.

My eyes widened at the sight of them: over three hundred and sixty pages of court records from both the trials. It wouldn't be easy to obtain the necessary permits for access to them, but I had just enough drachmas to tip just enough bureaucrats.

My family, immediate and extended, reacted strongly to my research. "It's a story that must be told," some said, "for Panayota, if for no other reason."

Others were less supportive. "Leave the dead alone," they said. "Let them lie peacefully in the cemetery of St Anthony."

There was one permission I felt I needed, but I could not get: Panayota's. It was the priest of my community in Stamford, Connecticut, who reassured me the book would be a memorial for Panayota.

Though initially I thought everything was in the court records or in the newspapers, I soon realized how incomplete the official story was. I would need to interview people—dozens and dozens of them, in Greece and America and elsewhere. Those most likely to remember the most, because of their age, turned out to be between eighteen and thirty years of age at the time of the murder. The youngest of my interviewees was seventy and the oldest ninety-six. I targeted the educated more, counting on them to elucidate the darkest areas. Big mistake. Education had absolutely nothing to do with how well people remembered, though it did have an impact on the kind of analysis the interviewees supplied.

I will remember fondly the wrinkled brows knitted in concentration as aging minds tried to capture elusive memories. Often, those who had supported George and Socrates couldn't recall important details. "It has been so long," they would say. "I have absolutely no memory of things." When the topic turned to events from the civil war, which preceded the murder, their memories were flawless.

One of my most revealing interviews took place in Athens in 2003 with Ntemy Mazarakis a defense attorney on both courts, by then more than eighty years old, who after several phone calls from America had finally relented and allowed me to visit her at her home. I had pored over the newspapers and the court records by then and was impressed with Ntemy' questions, each of which had invariably made an important point while at the same time sowing doubt among the jury.

November 12, 1954. George Nitsos (center) with Socrates (right), surrounded by their defense team, while the jury deliberates in Athens. The attorney with the hat is Ntemy Mazarakis. I interviewed her at her house in 2003. First from left is attorney Gunaris, and second is attorney Palos (with eyeglasses).

When I arrived at her home in Kiffisia, an exclusive Athens suburb, the sun was setting in the west.

Ntemy took me to the living room of her stately stone mansion and offered me orange juice. Dressed in a plaid skirt and sporting short hair, she appeared to be quite fit for her age. I could only marvel at her poise and aged beauty.

"What can I do for you, Dr. Konandreas?" she asked.

"Lukas, please, Mrs. Mazarakis," I replied.

"Ntemy," she said, correcting me.

Without saying a word, I removed from my bag a photo that had appeared in the *Acropolis* on November 12, 1954, decision day at the trial in Athens. The photo showed the defense team surrounding Nitsos and Karaiskos. Ntemy wore a hat.

"Is this creature me?" she asked, laughing. "Where did you unearth it from, Lukas?"

For the next two hours, while a huge storm rumbled overhead, we looked at photos and traded insights.

She remembered Thanasis as soon as she noticed his bold head in a photo. "Was he your father?" she asked.

"Yes," I replied.

"Oh, were we after him! Were we targeting him! But he kept slipping away..." She paused a moment before asking suddenly, "Is he alive?"

"No. It's been over fifteen years since he died."

I asked about the defense team's strategy, especially during the second trial in Halkida, when it became clear that the accused were going to be found guilty.

"You don't realize something," she said. "We all thought—I mean all six of us on the defense team thought—that Nitsos and Karaiskos were truly innocent."

"But surely..." I was incredulous.

"I know it sounds unbelievable with the hindsight you now have, but almost up to the time the verdict of 'guilty' came, we believed in their innocence. Nitsos and Karaiskos had indeed misled us. So the strategy that you now ask about—we based it on that assumption of innocence."

"I admit I'm no lawyer," I said, "but I know the case very well, having studied it in depth, and I find it hard to believe that six attorneys well versed in criminal law, forming what was arguably the best defense team for a criminal case in Greece at the time, were unable to sense that their clients were guilty. I would have expected a better plan to help the defendants."

"Near the end," she said, "we sensed it and tried to change our tactics, but the accused were not willing to even think about such a plan. Nitsos seemed to think that his money and the political power of his cousin, the journalist, and other important people were going to acquit him. He wouldn't admit the possibility of anything but a 'not guilty' plea. 'I'm completely innocent,' he used to say, 'and innocent means innocent, not innocent with diminished responsibility or any other lawyer's nonsense of that sort.' And that's what we set out to prove."

"That's unbelievable," I said, shaking my head.

"I remember," she said, combing her memory, "that night near the end of the trial when that woman, Nitsos's cousin, was on the witness stand."

"That would be Eudokia," I said.

"I don't remember her name now, but she told the court that

Panayota was always dressed by her husband in silk and that was the only way she would go out. At that point, the judge, who was extremely sharp, ordered the court clerks to open the box that contained the blood-spattered dress Panayota wore the night she was murdered. It was a robe, a cotton house robe. It didn't make sense that Panayota had changed into a robe if she had indeed planned to return later to the dinner party. I was the only defense attorney in the court that night, and it was very late. I saw the reaction of the jury, and I knew we were losing—and losing badly. It was almost midnight. When I got back from the court, I was confused and agitated, and I must have sounded so frantic that the other attorneys showed up immediately at the Paliria Hotel, where I was staying, when I phoned them to have a meeting."

"Why did you do that?" I asked.

"I wanted to explore a different scenario, one I had pondered before the trial in Athens, and see if we could present it, even at that late stage of the trial, as a true account of incidents."

"What was that scenario?" I asked eagerly.

"I wanted from the beginning to say that Nitsos was alone down at the Zakkas house and Panayota had stayed home. Then someone had taken her by force from their home and killed her by the ravine, and no one knew about it until Nitsos decided to leave the Zakkas home and walk toward his house and found her dead in the middle of the path."

I cocked my head in disbelief.

"Well, I know it didn't make sense," she said, reading the expression on my face, "but that tells you how misled, tired, agitated, desperate, almost out of reality I was by then, along with some of the other attorneys."

I thought of asking about Palos, whose closing remarks either intentionally or subconsciously had bordered on deranged. But I chose to keep quiet.

Ntemy then pieced together several inappropriate things George had done during the trial, including how he had misled his attorneys, and when I shared a few anecdotes that showed how he had behaved after being released from jail, she appeared shocked.

"Nitsos broke more commandments than Moses wrote," she said, to my amusement.

Perhaps depressed by the memory of everything he had done, she decided to change the topic.

"So tell me about yourself. I don't remember much about Thanasis Konandreas's family."

"Well, I have a sister and two brothers," I replied. "They all have good families."

Ntemy then asked me about the professions my siblings pursued and I told her.

"It's good that your father could afford all that," an impressed Ntemy said. "He was well off, as I remember."

I had to smile at that. "Well off he was not," I said, correcting her. "In fact, the prosecution attorneys almost did charitable work for Thanasis, and our family was left penniless after Halkida."

Then I told her about the free governmental policy that helped our education in the early '60's. "We were lucky, very fortunate," I concluded.

"No, no," Ntemy interrupted. "Your father possessed the fortitude and the honor to pursue justice against all odds. It seems that God has rewarded his good deeds through his children."

I thanked Ntemy and exited her house walking into the pelting rain her words of praise for my father resonating in my ears. As I drove back home to another suburb of the big city, my mind wondered through the names of people, besides my immediate family, who should also receive praise and thanks for their role in this story. I recognized many, but I placed at the top of my list the juror in the Athens trial, who after seven hours of jury arguments and likely pressures for the final verdict, did not hesitate to disagree with the other nine jurors who voted "Innocent." His dissenting vote opened the door for the second trial. On behalf of my aunt and father, thank you Demosthenes Dapontes.

DRAMATIS PERSONAE

BELOW IS A LIST OF names used in this book. Each name is followed by a short description of the person or location in question. Any person's name that differs from his or her real name is followed by the real name in parenthesis.

Aggeliki Gumas: Mother of Polyxeni Konandreas. Prosecution witness.

Aggelo (Aggeliki Kufasimis): Prosecution witness at Halkida. Sister of Thanasis Konandreas.

Alekos Tsipras (Alexandros Tsipras): Professor of literature. Cousin of Polyxeni Konandreas.

Alex Nitsos (Alexandros Nitsos): Brother of George Nitsos.

Alexandra (Alexandra Zakkas): Sister of Nitsos. Married to Miltiades Zakkas.

Amfissa: Capital of the prefecture of Fokida, within which Kupaki is located.

Antonakos (Georgios Kufasimis): Son of Aggelo. Cousin of Lukas Konandreas.

Apostolos (Apostolos Karandreas): Attorney, cousin, and confidante of Thanasis.

Basil (Vasilios Kolimbaris): Attorney. Prosecution witness on the second trial.

Dapontes, Demosthenes: Juror at the trial in Athens. Likely the only juror to dissent.

Demos (Demos Andreopoulos): Prosecution witness.

Effie (Efthemia Tsatuhas): Prosecution witness at the Halkida trial only.

Efthemia (Efthemia Konandreas): Mother of Thanasis Konandreas.

Eleftheria (Eleftheria Nitsos): Relative of George Nitsos, who got into an argument with Thanasis.

Eudokia (Eudokia Giannakopoulos): First cousin of Nitsos. Defense witness.

George Nitsos (Georgios Nitsos): Husband of Panayota. Also known by the nickname Linatsas.

Georges Gumas (Georgios Gumas): Brother of Polyxeni Konandreas. Brother-in-law of Thanasis.

Georgia: Wife of Dr. Lukas Konandreas, M.D., and a doctor herself.

Georgios Soulias: Panayota's father who died in the United States.

Giatros (Vasilios Koinis): Doctor. Son of Koinogiorgos of Kupaki. Married to Sofia.

Gunaris (Panagiotis Gunaris): Defense attorney.

Halkida: The city where the second trial took place.

Harry (Charalambos Stavropoulos): Prosecution witness.

John Gumas (Ioannis Gumas): Brother of Polyxeni Konandreas. Brother-in-law of Thanasis.

John Nitsos (Ioannes Nitsos): Father of George Nitsos. Settled in America. Married to Maria Nitsos.

Johnny (Ioannis Brumas): Son of Mary and Panaitakis.

Judge Demopulos: Judge at the Halkida court.

Kantas (Theodoros Kantas): The mailman Panayota grabbed the letter from.

Katina: Girlfriend of George Nitsos. Defense witness.

Karamitros (Georgios Karamitros): Cousin of Miltiades. Defense attorney.

Koinogeorgos (Georgios Koinis): Father of Giatros and uncle of Vuleftes.

Kokkinos (Apostolos Kokkinopoulos): Prosecution attorney.

Kostas (Kostas Konandreas): Son of Thanasis and Polyxeni Konandreas.

Krokylion: The bigger village next to Kupaki. Employed a police force and a doctor.

Kumes (Konstantinos Ioannou Kufasimis): Prosecution witness only at the second trial. The host of the youths' party on the night of the murder.

Kupaki: The village where the murder takes place.

Kutras (Panos Konandreas): Brother of Thanasis.

Lidoriki: Capital of the County, within which Kupaki is located.

Lukas Konandreas: Son of Thanasis and Polyxeni Konandreas. Went on to become Dr. Lukas Konandreas. Author of this book.

Maraveli: Area just outside the village where the Konandreases had their fields and animals.

Marula (Marula Mitsakis): The village woman who told Panayota about George Nitsos and Katina.

Mary (Maria Brumas): Wife of Panaitakis. Prosecution witness.

Metsios (Demetrios Soulias): Brother of Panayota

Miltiades (Miltiades Zakkas): Brother-in-law of George Nitsos. Married to his sister Alexandra.

Mitros (Demetrios Konandreas): Uncle of Thanasis. Lived next door to Thanasis in Kupaki.

Motsu: The site of a natural spring in Kupaki.

Nick (Nikolaos Pasios): The dance teacher. Married his student.

Ntemy Mazarakis (Despina Mazarakis): Defense attorney. Interviewed by author decades after trial.

Ntinos (Konstantinos Papaioannou): Village man and self-appointed jester. Prosecution witness.

Pagonis (Athanasios Pagonis): Shepherd in partnership with George Nitsos. Defense witness.

Palos (Ioannis Papakyriakopoulos): Attorney. Leader of the defense team.

Panaitakis (Panagiotis Brumas): Prosecution witness. Shepherd in partnership with George Nitsos and Thanasis Konandreas.

Panokostas (Kostas Konandreas): Father of Thanasis Konandreas.

Panos (Panos Konandreas): Son of Thanasis and Polyxeni Konandreas.

Pantulias (Konstantinos Pantulias): Married to a first cousin of Panayota. Defense witness.

Papadia (Vasiliki Papakonstantinou): Sister of Thanasis and wife of Papazois.

Papandreou (Limberis Papandreou): The public prosecutor at the Halkida trial.

Papazois (Zois Papakonstantinou): The village priest. Prosecution witness and Thanasis's brother-in-law.

Paraskevi (Paraskevi Soulias): Mother of Panayota.

Poly (Polyxeni Saitis): The young beauty who George Nitsos courted in the mid '40s.

Proedros (Konstantinos Georgiou Kufasimis): Defense witness. Accused of perjury, prosecuted, and found guilty.

Sakis: Criminal who Mary visited on behalf of Nitsos.

Socrates Karaiskos: George Nitsos's best man and close friend who stood trial along with him. Ultimately found guilty of murdering Panayota.

Sofia (Sofia Koinis): Wife of Giatros.

Thanasis (Thanasis Konandreas): Cousin of Panayota. Husband of Polyxeni. Father of Lukas Konandreas.

Tsipropanos (Panos Tsipras): Professor of Theology. Cousin of Polyxeni Konandreas.

Tsukalas (Aggelos Tsukalas): Prosecution attorney.

Vasilios (Vasilios Kalantzis): The man with whom George Nitsos had an ongoing feud. Prosecution witness.

Vuleftes (Georgios Koinis): Attorney and politician.

Zanias (Demetrios Zanias): Cousin of Katina Thema. Prosecution witness.

Zorianou: A village next to Kupaki.

Lukas Konandreas, December 2013

Lukas Konandeas M.D. one of four children, was born at Kupaki, a small mountain village in central Greece.

He finished elementary school there and high school in Athens Greece.

After graduating from the Medical School of the University of Athens, he migrated to Toronto Canada and from there he did Medical training in Chicago and Fresno California. He practiced Emergency Medicine in Sacramento California for about 6 years and from there he moved to Connecticut, where he organized an Urgent Care Center, which he still directs after 30 years.

He is married to Georgia, a Doctor of Psychology and has two sons.

Lukas Konandreas circa 1954

Thanasis Konandreas, in court March 1955   *Polyxeni Konandreas circa 1951*